EUROPE

ASIA

PACIFIC
OCEAN

AFRICA

INDIAN
OCEAN

AUSTRALASIA

OCEANIA

ANTARCTICA

WILDLIFE
FACT·FILE
yearbook

· 1992 ·

Above: A ground-dwelling, nocturnal hunter, the burrowing owl spends the day standing guard at the entrance to its home. This may be an abandoned underground burrow left by the prairie dog or the former den of some other species of American rodent.

Left: The male lion is a lazy creature, resting and sleeping by day and often relying on the lionesses within his pride to hunt for his food. He nevertheless arrives in time for the kill and takes first turn to gorge himself on the fresh meat.

WILDLIFE FACT·FILE
yearbook

1992

Foreword by

David Bellamy

Includes an interview with

Sir David Attenborough

First published in the UK in 1991 by International Masters Publishers Ltd
Winchester House, 259–269 Old Marylebone Road, London NW1 5RW

Copyright © 1991 International Masters Publishers Ltd

ISBN: 0 9518566 0 X

Edited, designed and typeset by The Book Creation Company, London:

Editor	*Sydney Francis*
Text editor	*Rachel Wright*
Research	*Rosalie Hoffmann*
Captions	*Nic Andrews*
Picture research	*Jackum Brown, Vicky Walters*
Art director	*Ron Samuels*
Design assistants	*Keith Davis, Errol Campbell*
Typesetting and production consultant	*Alan Slingsby*
Wildlife consultant	*Jonathan Elphick*
Editorial consultant	*Tony Hare*
Conservation consultant	*Jaqueline Karas*
Maps	*Michael Hill*
Graph illustration	*Pinkbarge/Alec Hitchens*
Colour reproduction	*Kestrel Lithographic Reproductions, Essex*

Printed and bound by Arnoldo Mondadori, Verona, Italy

The map of the world is drawn to the Peter's Projection.

Every effort has been made to use environmentally friendly materials in the production of this book. The paper contains 50 per cent recycled fibres and was pulped and bleached using acid-free substances. Oxygen was used in the bleaching process, avoiding the use of environmentally damaging chemicals. The boards were manufactured from 100 per cent recycled materials.

The publishers would also like to thank Louise Bostock and Hal Robinson for their help and advice.

In Association with the *Wildlife Fact-File* Team

Publishing manager	*Deborah Clarke*
Consultant editor	*John Birdsall*
Production controller	*Suzie Hutton*
Picture editor	*Mira Connolly*
Art editor	*Frank Landamore*
Senior sub-editor	*Matthew Turner*
Senior designers	*Neil Rigby, Colin Hawes*
Sub-editors	*Geoff Barker, Hanna Bolus, Vicky Hanson, Suzanne Jones*
Production assistant	*Stefan Podhorodecki*

Authenticators

Paul Bright BSc Phd
Bristol University

Dr Pat Morris BSc PhD
Lecturer, Department of Biology, Royal Holloway and Bedford New College

Alexandra Dixon MSc
Conservation co-ordinator and assistant to the General Director, Zoological Society of London

Bob Scott
Head of Reserves Management, RSPB

Dr Richard Wall BSc PhD
Research Associate, Bristol University

Dr John Feltwell BSc PhD FRES FLS
Naturalist

J. Bryan Carroll BSc CBiol MIBiol
Curator of Mammals, Jersey Wildlife Preservation Trust

Simon Tonge BSc
Section Head, Reptile House, Jersey Wildlife Preservation Trust

Dr Angela Milner BSc
Research Scientist, Natural History Museum

CONTENTS

CONTRIBUTORS

These pages: With its long neck outstretched in front and equally long legs extending behind, the pink flamingo in flight is a most spectacular sight. These birds were photographed over the Camargue in southern France.

Jill Bailey (MA Oxon) has written over 40 children's books and several adult books. She has also written and produced videos for the BBC, some of which have won awards.

Adrian Barnett (MA Oxon, MSc) has worked in rainforests in west Africa and in the Andes and the Amazon in South America. Over the past decade he has discovered several new animal and plant species and rediscovered various others.

Hanna Bolus (MA Oxon) is a writer and editor on conservation and environmental issues. She is currently involved in the *Wildlife Fact-File*.

Duncan Brewer is a full-time writer whose specializations include natural history, earth sciences, Third World issues and investigative journalism. He has recently completed a series of astronomy books for children.

Mark Cocker (BA) is a professional author and naturalist. His publications include a biography of the ornithologist Richard Meinertzhagen and a co-authored study of the nineteenth-century naturalist Brian Hodgson.

Rick Gould (BSc, PhD, MIBiol, CBiol) is an environmental biologist with extensive knowledge of conservation and air pollution. He has worked in environmental management in the USA, Sweden, New Zealand and the UK.

Suzanne Jones (BA) is a writer and editor, currently involved in the *Wildlife Fact-File*.

John Lythgoe (MA, PhD, ScD) trained as a botanist at Cambridge University, but after taking his PhD, he began researching into the vision of aquatic animals. He is now a senior research fellow at Bristol University working on colour vision in fish.

Sara Oldfield (BA) has worked for the Nature Conservancy Council, Royal Botanic Gardens, Kew and as a conservation consultant. She has spent the last three years collecting information on rare tropical timber species for the World Conservation Monitoring Centre.

Fred Pearce is an environmental journalist and author specializing in international issues. He is an author of books on acid rain, the greenhouse effect and environmental campaigning. His next book, *The Dammed*, on water politics, will be published during 1992. He is a regular contributor to *New Scientist*, *The Guardian* and BBC *Wildlife* magazine.

Nigel Sitwell edited *Wildlife* magazine (now renamed *BBC Wildlife*) for 16 years, and travels widely reporting on wildlife and the environment. In 1979, he was awarded the Order of the Golden Ark by Prince Bernhard of the Netherlands for services to wildlife conservation.

Colin Tudge is a zoologist who works as a writer and broadcaster, mainly for *New Scientist* and BBC Radio. His latest book, *Last Animals at the Zoo*, was published by Hutchinson Radius in September 1991.

Elizabeth Wood (PhD) is a consultant marine biologist with a particular interest in coral reef ecology and conservation. She is an experienced scuba diver and underwater photographer.

John Woodward (BA) has been photographing and writing about wildlife for many years. His main interest is insects and creepy-crawlies, particularly spiders.

Steven Yearley is Professor of Sociology at the University of Ulster in Belfast, where he does research on the politics of the green movement in Britain and Ireland. His recent work is outlined in his book *The Green Case*, published in 1991.

CONSULTANTS

Jonathan Elphick (BSc) is a natural history editor, consultant and author. He writes regularly on birds for the *Wildlife Fact-File*. His current work includes writing a series of bird books and editing the book of a major new BBC TV series on the natural history of Russia.

Jacqueline H W Karas (BA) joined Friends of the Earth in 1991, having spent eight years at the Climatic Research Unit at the University of East Anglia. She has acted as a consultant to environmental and conservation groups, the media and a number of publications.

Tony Hare (PhD) is a writer, scriptwriter, and environmentalist. He was principal ecologist at the London Ecology Unit, and is now a leading light in TV environment programmes, starting *Going Live*'s Greenline, and a consultant and scriptwriter on *A Beetle Called Derek*. He also chairs the board of Plantlife.

FOREWORD

A wildlife year book! Essential reading in a world where natural habitat and wilderness is being destroyed at the rate of more than one hectare each second and the rate of extinction is escalating all the time.

However, 1991 saw a number of breakthroughs, the most important of which was the signing of the Antarctic Treaty affording protection to the great frozen continent for at least the next 50 years. Hooray for Greenpeace and all the other tireless campaigners who have worked to that end. We must all now work even harder to ensure that the great green summit to be held in Brazil in 1992 carries on the good work, on a worldwide scale, working for a sustainable future.

Please read the book with care and through it begin to understand the complexity and wonder of the living world around us. Then remember the awesome fact that, by the end of this century, which is now only eight years away, your world is going to have to support six billion other people, each one of whom has an equal right to their fair share of the earth's resources.

The fact that you are reading this book means that, in all probability, you are one of the rich one-third of the world's population who use 80 per cent of all the resources and cause much of the pollution.

Flick through the book and look at the pictures. Do you want your children and grandchildren to have to try and live in a world devoid of much of that wildlife?

Let 1992 be your wildlife resolution year. Save energy, walk to school if you can, support your local wildlife trust and hence your local wildlife, and join at least one of the national and international organizations, such as BTCV, FoE, Greenpeace, the National Trust or RSPB.

Thank you for caring

David J Bellamy
The Conservation Foundation
1 Kensington Gore
London SW7 2AR

Right: The steep slopes of the Ngorongoro crater in Tanzania offer one of the richest and most remarkable wildlife habitats in the whole of the African continent. The area is to be the subject of a film entitled *Kingdom of the Black God,* made by Richard Matthews and due for release at the end of 1991.

INTRODUCTION

The *Wildlife Fact-File Yearbook* is an innovative publication that presents an exciting survey of the latest developments in the world of wildlife in an easily readable and beautifully illustrated form. It is in the nature of such a book to be topical, and we have tried to ensure that the information it contains is as up-to-date and accurate as possible. An impressive team of expert authors, interviewers, editors, designers, artists and photographers has been drawn together to create this unique and indispensable companion to the *Wildlife Fact-File* series.

The scope of this pioneering yearbook is wide, ranging from the latest news about the giant panda and surprising discoveries about sharks and magpies, through beautiful and informative photo-essays on courtship, hunting, mating and camouflage, to accounts of the problems facing coral reefs, wetlands and Antarctica. There is a penetrating analysis of the crisis currently facing zoos, a behind-the-scenes examination of natural history museums, reviews of 30 years of conservation campaigning and an analysis of the effects on wildlife of the Gulf War.

Building on the solid bank of information presented in the *Wildlife Fact-File*, the *Yearbook* is able to take you on a journey of discovery with in-depth articles and a wealth of superb full-colour photographs and artwork, none of which appear in the cards. In fascinating interviews, people who devote their lives to wildlife reveal their motivations and explain what their work involves. David Attenborough shares with us some of the dramas behind the making of the *Trials of Life* and his other award-winning BBC TV natural history series.

The Green Pages include an invaluable diary of wildlife and environmental events over the last two years, and details of coming events in 1992. A classified list of wildlife and conservation organizations in the UK, Europe and worldwide, complete with a description of each one and details of how to become involved, is also included, together with a survey of opportunities for enjoying wildlife study and conservation as a lifelong interest or profession, from courses to competitions. All this, and more, are in this 'first' of a book.

Whatever your interest in wildlife and whether you follow this interest from the comfort of your armchair or by going out and watching the animals first hand, this book will give you and your family many hours of enjoyment. Used together with your collection of *Wildlife Fact-File* cards, it will provide an invaluable source of information and ready reference to help you and your children to understand what is happening in the ever-changing world of wildlife.

Jonathan Elphick
Tony Hare
Jacqueline Karas

Opposite: The crab-eater seal is one of only four seals to be found in the Antarctic. All are carnivorous, but each has a different diet so that they can co-exist fairly peacefully in the same waters. The peace is only relative, however, as the fearsome leopard seal sometimes preys on its smaller relatives, including the crab-eater seal.

Above: The tiger hunts by stealth, attacking its prey from the side or the rear. Its camouflaging stripes help to conceal its approach until it is too late for many victims, including this hapless monkey.

Animals of the World

There may be in excess of 50 million species in the animal kingdom, but only a small fraction of these have so far been discovered and classified. Our knowledge of many is confused and sketchy and constantly in need of revision, with new research and discoveries occurring all the time.

This section celebrates the glorious diversity of the world's wildlife, beginning with what many people see as the symbol of conservation, the giant panda. It looks at new animal and plant discoveries, and recent research into wildlife, including the giant octopus — a gentle, inquisitive creature — and naked mole rats. Three articles give an insight into the lives of animals and plants that live in extreme conditions, namely the desert, the polar regions and the deep sea. The section then looks at the variety of ways in which animals mate, hunt and camouflage themselves, before returning to the problem of wildlife in danger, discussing the threats to our natural heritage.

Left: The pale chanting goshawk is confined to the woodland savannah of Africa, where it eats lizards, small snakes, frogs and insects. It hunts them on foot, chasing its prey along the ground.

Below left: A young tiger is not born with hunting skills and needs to acquire these from its mother in order to survive. It stays with her for the first two or three years of its life and learns from her example before finally setting off to fend for itself.

Below: The sidewinder rattlesnake has heat-sensitive organs on either side of its head. These enable it to sense infra-red radiation and thus hunt warm-blooded prey in complete darkness.

PANDAS IN PERIL

Opposite: The giant panda was unknown in the West until the French missionary-explorer Armand David discovered it in 1869. Now it is perhaps the most familiar and best-loved of all the world's 1.8 million named species.

The giant panda enjoys a rather special status as a symbol of wildlife conservation — largely due to the World Wildlife Fund (now called the World Wide Fund for Nature or WWF) having adopted a stylized panda as its logo. The panda now has the added distinction of being arguably the world's most expensive endangered species. The WWF has contributed more than £2,106,000 to giant panda conservation since 1980, in addition to the substantial sums spent by the Chinese government.

Recently there has been considerable public criticism of WWF for spending so much on a single animal species, apparently without a great deal of success. WWF was forced to admit that the 10-year campaign had not resulted in any increase in the number of giant pandas in the wild; indeed, the total may actually have declined. Current estimates of the total population hover between 800 and 1000. So has all this money been wasted? It is an important question, but to answer it requires an understanding of the animal's way of life.

A million years ago the giant panda inhabited a wide area of China, extending into what is now Myanmar. But as the climate became drier and humans began to encroach on its habitat it gradually retreated into its last stronghold, a relatively small area of bamboo forest in the mountains on the edge of the Tibetan plateau.

The giant panda has long featured in Chinese literature and legend. More than 1000 years ago a Tang dynasty poet suggested that the animal had magical properties and that a screen painted with pandas would ward off evil spirits. Unknown in the West until 1869, the first westerners to shoot a giant panda were two sons of the American President Theodore Roosevelt, Theodore Jr and Kermit, in 1928.

Even as late as the 1970s, very little was known about the giant panda's biology or behaviour. Captive pandas had barely been studied and their way of life in the wild was more or less a closed book. But research was stimulated by an event which occurred in 1975 in northern Sichuan Province, in the heart of panda country. In that year there was a massive die-off of bamboo which led to the death by starvation of around 150 giant pandas. Alarmed Chinese officials organized a census which suggested that only about 1000 of the animals remained.

The problem was not caused by man, but by an unusual feature of bamboo biology. Although bamboos reproduce very successfully by vegetative means, they flower and produce seed only once in their lives. Then they die. Furthermore, some internal clock causes most of the plants in a given species to flower and die at about the same time. The life cycle of bamboo varies according to the species, and in the case of umbrella bamboo — the species that died

Below: The giant panda has roamed over parts of China and Tibet for more than a million years. Fewer than 1000 individuals now remain, confined to fairly inaccessible regions.

in 1975 — it appears to be 100 years. The giant pandas in Sichuan eat about 20 species of bamboo, of which only four are really favoured. In the area where so many pandas died, only umbrella bamboo was available. In other parts of the panda's range, additional species are normally available. But because of increasing human population and the cultivation of more and more land in the giant panda's domain, the animals were confined to pockets of forest and could not migrate to areas where food was more plentiful.

Recognition of these problems prompted the Chinese to join forces with WWF in 1980 in a massive project to protect the giant panda. The first step was to find out more about the animal so that an effective conservation programme could be devised. These studies were focused on Wolong Natural Reserve, located north-west of Chengdu, the capital of Sichuan Province, and the largest and most important of China's 12 giant panda reserves. Over the past decade many western and Chinese scientists have participated in this research, which has greatly increased our knowledge of giant pandas.

They are aggressively solitary animals, except during March and April when the females are on heat for about three days and

Below: In recent years, it has been less the activities of humans than the natural disappearance of several species of bamboo that has threatened the giant panda's continued existence.

allow males to approach them. They occupy territories of about 2sq km on average; in winter they range more widely, having to descend to lower altitudes in search of unfrozen streams from which to drink.

One perennial mystery about the giant panda is where it fits into the animal kingdom. Is it more closely related to raccoons or to bears? Scientists are divided. Studies of its blood suggest affinities with the bears, but chromosome studies place it with the raccoons.

Although the giant panda is classified as a carnivore, it seems to be slowly evolving into a vegetarian. While its huge muscular jaws and broad serrated molars are well adapted to crunching up tough bamboo, it has a remarkably short intestinal tract, typical of a carnivore but quite inappropriate

for its herbivorous lifestyle. Its inadequate digestive apparatus causes up to 50 per cent of the bamboo it eats to pass through undigested. This inefficiency explains why the giant panda needs to eat so much — about 20kg per day. Another clue to its origin as a meat-eater is that, although the panda finds it hard to catch other animals, it will readily eat any small creature it does manage to get hold of. Indeed, when scientists need to trap live pandas for research purposes, the most effective bait is cooked pork.

A lot of the information about panda behaviour, especially their feeding, was gathered by laboriously tracking them and observing what they had eaten. Other valuable data was gleaned by analysing their large droppings. However, as the American zoologist and joint project leader Dr George Schaller pointed out, 'There are limits to the amount of excitement that contemplation of a dropping can provide.' So a number of pandas have been fitted with radio transmitters mounted on collars around their necks. The signals enable researchers to plot the animals' movements on a map, and also to tell when they are active or resting.

In the wild, female pandas normally raise only one cub every two years, though not all the young survive. At birth, the youngsters weigh about 100g. But they grow quickly, reaching 28kg in nine months. Adults weigh 90–115kg and have virtually no predators, although young pandas are sometimes taken by leopards and wild dogs. If their rate of reproduction in the

Above: Panda country is now a fraction of the size it once was. Those pandas that survive live at a height of 2000–3200m on the edge of the Tibetan plateau.

wild is relatively low, in captivity it is even less. For some reason, giant pandas breed very poorly in captivity. Only 15 have been born outside China: five in Washington National Zoo in America, and seven in Mexico City's Chapultepec Zoo. The other births were in Tokyo and Madrid. None of the American cubs survived more than four days, though four of the Mexican offspring are still alive. Nobody can think of a good reason why smoggy Mexico City should do better than zoos elsewhere, although it does happen to be at about the same altitude as the pandas' natural habitat in western China. There have been births in Chinese zoos, but only one has been born so far in the expensive breeding centre built at Wolong, and that quickly died.

It seems, therefore, that captive breeding is not the answer to giant panda survival. And the animal's prospects in the wild are by no means encouraging. It is confined to small, isolated pockets of natural habitat, may suffer from inbreeding, reproduces slowly, and depends on a nutritionally poor food supply that is liable to disappear periodically. Although ranking alongside the

Great Wall as an important part of China's heritage, it is still captured by poachers who risk the death penalty to supply a ready market for skins in Japan and Taiwan.

Part of the WWF panda project has involved training field researchers and rangers, who are badly needed because of a threefold increase in the number of China's protected areas over the last five years. However, this training programme has not been without its difficulties. Some of the courses were poorly attended, with participants pleading sickness or a sudden need to visit ailing relatives in distant cities. On the whole, the Chinese do not seem to find the life of a field naturalist or ranger as appealing as westerners do. Not many are as dedicated as Professor Hu Jinchu, China's leading panda expert, who agrees that it can be a difficult life but adds that 'Luckily I find happiness in hardship!'

The latest proposals by WWF and its Chinese counterparts include measures to increase the number of panda reserves from 12 to 25, which would mean that nearly half of the 11,000sq km of panda habitat would be protected; to maintain or re-establish bamboo corridors between patches of panda habitat; to improve anti-poaching patrols; and to halt logging, as well as forest clearance by villagers, in panda country.

At this point it is relevant to return to the question of whether WWF should have spent, or should continue to spend, large sums on an animal whose chances of long-term survival seem uncertain. It is true that wildlife conservation worldwide is desperately short of funds, and it would be easy to find other ways to spend this money. But many other large mammals have a precarious status — rhinos, elephants, tigers, gorillas and orang-utans, to name just a few — although none of these is as poorly adapted to withstand change as the panda. Should we abandon them all? One could argue that, from an ecological point of view, the extinc-

Below: The giant panda has to eat about 20kg of bamboo each day and spends up to 12 hours feeding, at regular intervals, throughout the day and night.

tion of the giant panda might not make much difference. But we cannot be sure.

WWF regarded the giant panda project as its entry ticket into China, and while the costly and grandiose research laboratory and breeding centre at Wolong (which the WWF was obliged to finance) was certainly a mistake, many positive results have come from the overall programme. The exposure of Chinese scientists to modern methods of wildlife research and nature reserve management is a good example. Another is that 'saving the panda' actually means saving much more. Consider Wolong itself. It is a wild and magical land of spectacular natural beauty. Within the reserve's 2000sq km are more than 100 peaks over 5000m high (the highest is 6200m). It is a botanist's paradise, with trees, shrubs and wild flowers covering every available surface in exuberant profusion.

Wolong is also a refuge for many rare and interesting animals. There are wolves and Asiatic wild dogs, and a number of cats, including spotted, clouded and snow leopards. There is the lesser (or red) panda; pheasants of several species; musk deer; black bears; a trio of strange goat-antelopes (goral, serow and takin); groups of beautiful blue-faced golden monkeys; and, above the snow line, herds of magnificent blue sheep. And that is just one reserve that benefits from WWF involvement.

There is one other aspect worthy of consideration. Saving the panda — or trying to — surely has a symbolic significance for WWF itself, as well as a deep cultural importance for the Chinese. Not to mention an emotional, even sentimental, appeal for other people around the world.

And it is worth reflecting on what the giant panda's status would be today if WWF had never become involved. The chances are that the species would be a lot worse off. WWF is now a rich organization, with a total annual expenditure on conservation of nearly £70 million. It should not waste money, of course, and it cannot save every species that is endangered — but millions of people would be shocked if it were to abandon the giant panda in its time of need.

Nigel Sitwell

THE WILDLIFE DETECTIVES

Above: The golden age of animal discovery may be over, and new primates, such as this monkey, may not often be found, but they are still appearing at a steady rate. This is the yellow-tailed woolly monkey, discovered by Dr Russell Mittermeier in the Andes in Peru, South America.

In total, around 1.8 million species of animals and plants have been scientifically named, although there are thought to be between 30 and 80 million species on earth. No one is exactly sure because most are thought to occur in tropical regions, particularly tropical rainforests, and these are the parts of the world that have been studied least.

Most animals are insects, most insects are tropical and most live in the treetops of the tropical rainforest. Recent studies found 3000 species of insect in just 10 trees in the rainforests of Borneo, many of them new to science, and two scientists from the Natural History Museum in London recently described over 800 new insects they had collected in a small area of one national park in Sulawesi, in Indonesia.

If insects are still being discovered at a great rate, but are mostly small and easily overlooked, what about larger creatures? Do people still discover new mammals and birds? The answer is, 'Yes, but not as often as they used to.' For both groups, the golden years of discovery were the late nineteenth century, when imperial expansion made it easier to reach previously inaccessible corners of the globe. All the big mammals had been discovered by the 1930s — the last, the kouprey, was described in 1937. The species which are discovered now, at the rate of two to three a year, are mostly tropical bats, rodents, shrews or marsupials. Since 1934, 134 new species of bird have been described. Most have been small, brown and tropical.

Not all the new species are like this, however, and the stories of how some of these species came to be discovered are amazing. It is, of course, impossible to predict when a new species will be found, but good detective work can help. Dr Russell Mittermeier was just such a biologist turned sleuth. In 1974, while working in the remote foothills of the Peruvian Andes, he noticed the skin of an unknown species of monkey being used as a saddle on a trader's horse. Though the skin was tattered and worn it looked like that of Humboldt's woolly monkey, a species of the lower Amazon — but not quite the same. The body colour was slightly different and the tail was yellow, as distinct from the black of Humboldt's. Enquiries revealed that the monkey, known locally as the pacu-runtu or tupamono, was to be found in the northern Peruvian Andes, though it was rarely seen.

Right: The distinction between two different but closely related animals and regional variations of the same species is a process fraught with potential problems. The fork-marked lemur, widely distributed throughout Madagascar, was considered to be one species, but now has sufficient variations in colour and patterning to be thought of as several separate species.

After several abortive expeditions through thick jungle, Dr Mittermeier and his colleagues found the monkey. As they suspected, it was a new species, which they named the yellow-tailed woolly monkey. A conservation scheme has now been started to ensure its future survival.

Dr Mittermeier's discovery was unusual for two reasons. First because, at around 7kg, the species was comparatively large and, second, because there had been no previous rumours of its existence. For an animal as noticeable as a monkey there are normally local rumours and stories to alert the biologist. Such stories did, however, help two young Brazilian biologists, Maria Lucia Lorini and Vanessa Persson, to find a new species of lion tamarin in southern Brazil. The lion tamarins are a very special group of small monkeys. Belonging to the genus *Leontopithecus*, they are all restricted to the Atlantic coastal forests on the country's eastern seaboard. Each weighs about 650g and is around 100cm from nose to tail tip. All species have long, glossy, silky fur, and are either gold all over, black over the body with a gold face or black with a gold bottom. There were, however, persistent rumours of a fourth species, gold with a black head. As the stories came from the region around São Paulo, Brazil's biggest city, they were dismissed by most people, for all the forest in the region had been cut down or disturbed long ago. However,

Below: Vast expanses of rainforest, like this area on St Lucia, have yet to be properly explored. Lurking within such places are millions of animal and plant species, many of which may never have been seen before.

Right: The Balbina white spiny rat, a relative of this common Guyana spiny rat, will probably never be seen again. Six white spiny rats were discovered recently during the building of the Balbina Dam in Brazil, but all died soon after and the area from which they came is now 10m under water.

Dante Martins Teixeira believed them, and continued to collect reports. Gradually he pieced the story together. Then, in 1990, while working on the small offshore island of Superagui, Lorini and Persson, colleagues of Teixeira, found a specimen of a black-headed lion tamarin lying dead beside a road. The local stories were vindicated and, appropriately, the new black-faced lion tamarin was given the Latin name *Leontopithecus caissara*, after the *caissaras* or local fishermen who were the source of much of the information Teixeira had used to pinpoint the likely site. Subsequently they helped Lorini and Persson find the new micro-monkey in the wild and it is now known that some 200 of these little animals exist, on a small island just off the coast of one of the biggest cities in the world.

On the other side of the world, in Madagascar, another new primate was recently discovered. The golden bamboo lemur, a medium-sized lemur weighing 1.5kg, with orange body fur, a black face and yellow eyebrows, chest and throat, was found by a joint American-Madagascan team near the village of Rafomona in the south-eastern part of the country. Living in dense bamboo forests, it had escaped detection for years because of the inhospitable nature of its habitat. But if the animal's existence excited scientists, its diet astonished them. The lemur lives on a diet of young bamboo shoots, which are packed with cyanide to deter less specialist predators. The concentration of poison in a single shoot would be enough to kill a man, yet the lemur, which chomps its way through several shoots a day, somehow manages to detoxify its potentially lethal meal.

Not all human studies of animals are so objective. One discovery in Gabon was the result of a group of hunters' very practical interest in monkeys as food. However, as their catch was waiting to be cooked, a British zoologist who was visiting the region happened to come into their camp. He saw the monkey, recognized it for what it was and bought it from the hunters. The new species is astonishingly beautiful, with elegant body colours set off by a long golden-yellow tail. This feature has given it both its Latin name, *Cercopithecus solatus*, and its common one, the sun-tailed guenon. It is thought to be very rare and live high up in undisturbed forest. As yet no zoologist has seen a living specimen.

With some species it is unlikely that a living specimen will ever be seen again, as their scientific discovery coincided with their probable extinction. This is the case with the Balbina white spiny rat. This, a naturally pale relative of the common Guyana spiny rat, was discovered in 1988 during the operation to rescue animals from the area being flooded by the construction of Brazil's Balbina Dam. Six animals were found huddled on a small hill just above the rising floodwaters. Shocked and starving, they all died later in captivity. The area they came from is now under 10m of water and, since the rats are poor climbers, it seems unlikely that any further specimens escaped the inundation. For other species, the scientists arrived just too late. The team that discovered Madagascar's golden bamboo lemur in 1987 also received reports of a 'red bamboo lemur' from village elders. Visitors to the site, about 170km north of that where the golden lemur was found, found that all the bamboo forests had been destroyed. The chances of tracing the red bamboo lemur now appear slim indeed.

Not everything that is originally described as a new species proves to be one, however. In 1989, exciting reports began to filter out of Borneo that a new species of river dolphin had been found. A French biologist, François-Xavier Pelletier, hearing local reports, had travelled to the almost unexplored Mahakam River region of eastern Borneo. After months of work he finally brought out living specimens from the Jempang-Melitany lakes and deposited them in a local aquarium. If genuine, this would have been a remarkable discovery: the first new river dolphin for 34 years and a considerable extension to the known range of the group, from two rivers in South America, one in India and one in China. Unfortunately, detailed analysis showed that the two dolphins were just very large young specimens of the finless porpoise, a well-known species of Borneo's river estuaries that does occasionally migrate up rivers.

Concern for the conservation of individual rare specimens has led to calls for a change in accepted practices of species description which require that a dead specimen be prepared for study and description by museum experts. This movement began in the late 1970s when a new species of petrel was photographed. Though obviously different from all other petrels, its validity was not accepted until a specimen was procured. This situation is, thankfully, now changing. Recently, a new species of shrike from Somalia, the Bulo Burti boubou, was described using just photographs and analyses of its blood proteins. The bird was then returned to the original area and released from captivity. Since blood proteins are just as precise a way of identifying species as the classical descriptions of plumage and bone

Below: The blind Andean shrew is the world's most southerly shrew. It was thought to be extremely rare until a team from Oxford University discovered that their predecessors had simply been looking in all the wrong places. In fact, it is abundant within its chosen domain in Ecuador's El Cajas National Park.

Above: The black-faced lion tamarin was only officially discovered in 1990 when a juvenile female of a species not previously classified was found lying by the side of the road, having been killed by a car.

structure, this life-preserving technique offers hope for the non-destructive discovery of new species in the future. In honour of this, the scientists named the species *Laniarius liberatus,* 'the freed shrike'.

The rediscovery of a species thought to be lost or extinct can be a frustrating, but rewarding, business. Known to science only since 1957, when eight skulls were collected from villagers in Nimba County, eastern Liberia, the Liberian mongoose had never been seen alive by scientists. As mining, logging and road construction had occurred over much of eastern Liberia, there were doubts as to whether it still survived. In 1990, Mark Taylor organized an expedition to find out. During weeks of work in the newly created Sapo National Park he caught several mongooses, but only common ones. Taylor began to search more widely, visiting other areas of the country and questioning villagers and hunters. Twice he was directed to villages which reputedly had a skin. On both occasions it turned out that the skin had recently been destroyed. Eventually, however, Taylor had luck (of sorts), managing to obtain one animal that had been shot that morning and was being roasted on an open fire. The fur was burnt, but the animal was recognizable from its teeth. Now sure of its continuing existence, Taylor plans to return

to try again in the hope of capturing live specimens and setting up a breeding colony for this obviously endangered mammal.

When searching for rare or little-known species, local knowledge is of key importance. It is, however, vital to ask the right question of the right person. This was demonstrated by the experience of the French ornithologists, Lucienne Wilné and Olivier Langrand, who were searching for the slender-billed flufftail in Madagascar in 1989. Known from only 17 specimens and last seen in 1930, this rail (a distant relative of the moorhen) was known to be a marshland specialist, living in dense reed swamps and other wetlands and dense vegetation at altitudes of between 950 and 1800m. Working in the marshlands south of the capital of Antananarivo, Wilné and Langrand were frustrated by the persistent failure of their questioning of male hunters, all of whom denied that the bird existed. It was only when the ornithologists turned to the women of the region that they were rewarded. The flufftail is well known to the local women, who call it *manganahitra.* They see it when they go to the marshes to collect reeds for baskets and mats. The men rarely, if ever, visit the marshlands. With the help of the local women, Wilné and Langrand were able to find, photograph and release the flufftail — the first sighting for over 60 years.

Not all rediscoveries are the result of deliberate searching; some come as a complete surprise. On 7 September 1989, Fernando and Cacilda Carvalho, members of the Rio de Janeiro Birdwatcher's Club, saw a bird they could not identify in a forest in Rio de Janeiro State. They described it to J. Fernando Paxeco, an expert on the region's birds. On 24 September Paxeco and Fernando Carvalho returned to the site and found a pair of black-hooded antwrens. The last reliable record for this tiny bird had been from the second half of the nineteenth century. Along with several other species, it had been feared extinct as a result of forest destruction around Rio.

Another example of a rediscovery that resulted from being in the right place at the right time is that of the Madagascar serpent eagle. After not having been seen since 1930, a specimen flew near to Cambridge University's Will Duckworth and Ben Sheldon while they were in Madagascar's eastern rainforests and stayed long enough for them to be able to make a detailed description. This confirmed that the eagle still lives — 58 years after its last sighting.

What, then, is the value of all this hard and often dangerous work? Can animals not survive perfectly well even if we do not know about them? From the fact that some species are rediscovered many years after their original description, it would certainly seem so. But in a world of limited financial and technical resources, where rates of habitat loss and human population are increasing, new and rediscovered species have a very important role to play. They are newsworthy and generate awareness and publicity for conservation efforts. They encourage international cooperation and let local people know that what they have is special. Such 'high profile' species can even be the reason for the establishment of new protected areas. This has happened with the lion tamarins, the golden bamboo lemur and several species of bird. These programmes, although focused on a single species, help to protect all the species resident in the area.

If the species is especially charismatic it may form the focus of an environmental education campaign. This has been the case with Peru's yellow-tailed woolly monkey, with the government launching a conservation awareness drive to commemorate the tenth anniversary of its discovery. While it may be argued that the money spent would have been better put toward practical fieldwork or even towards solving the social

problems that cause conservation crises in the first place, it cannot be denied that new and rediscovered species provide a focus that helps to make everyone aware of the irretrievable natural heritage that we have just begun to explore and are in great danger of losing. Rather than some glorious and exotically plumaged bird, it is perhaps the Balbina white spiny rat, the last few shivering representatives facing drowning as the result of a development they neither under-stood nor caused, which should be the symbol of all such species — both those that are known and those yet to be found.

Adrian Barnett

Above: The description of the golden-crowned lemur by E. L. Simons in 1988 ended a long saga of uncertainty. It had been found in 1974, but was thought to be simply a well-marked local variety. Simons' detailed observations revealed the real identity of this placid white-furred leaf-eater from the dry forests of north-east Madagascar.

NEW RESEARCH ON WILDLIFE

Opposite: The giant octopus propels itself by squirting water behind it. Some of the octopuses filmed appeared to enjoy playing hide-and-seek with the divers.

Below: All the octopuses studied the divers carefully with their highly developed eyes. Giant octopuses have the largest brain of any invertebrate.

Some of the most interesting new research carried out into wildlife shows us familiar subjects in an unfamiliar light. Sometimes the result is to rehabilitate the reputation of creatures popularly thought to be dangerous or pests. Much new work is now presented in film and popular book form, as well as in academic journals. But behind the gloss are often many years of close observation of creatures in the wild and sometimes in controlled situations in the laboratory. This helps expand public awareness of the animal world and the problems it faces, and can increase pressure on governments, business operations and individuals to act more responsibly towards the creatures they exploit and displace.

Octopus dofleini is, like a character from a Jules Verne adventure story or a vintage Tarzan film, a giant octopus that can reach a weight of 70kg, with an armspan of over 7m. British film-makers Victoria Stone and Mark Deeble specialize in marine wildlife, and their film, *Devil Fish*, shot off the northwest coast of the USA, effectively destroys the myth of the giant octopus as an aggressive monster. Far from picking unwary sailors from the decks of passing ships or hauling divers off to underwater caves to devour them, the giant octopus is shown to be a gentle, intelligent and inquisitive creature. Feeding mainly on shellfish, it tends to treat humans as potential playmates rather than potential snacks. Mark Deeble filmed Victoria Stone deliberately coming into close contact with a giant octopus, and becoming entwined in its long, powerful tentacles, with their double rows of white suckers.

Like other octopus species, the giant octopus paralyses its prey by injecting venom, after biting with its parrot-like beak or drilling through any shell with its radula, or toothed tongue. Much to the film-makers' relief, the octopus made no attempt to bite, but instead explored the surface of the strange diving creature in the Neoprene dry-suit, being particularly enraptured when it discovered areas of bare skin. Stone and Deeble's work has

Right: Observers have watched the killer whales of the Valdés Peninsula teaching their young how to carry out the beaching and relaunching operation, practising the manoeuvres over and over again on deserted beaches.

Below: The bulging pressure wave generated by the passage of the huge predators throws baby sea lions forward on to the beach, and the killer whales follow them, deliberately beaching their great bodies.

demonstrated to large TV audiences that people have nothing to fear from the giant octopus, a lesson that should benefit both.

In a similarly risky venture, the divers who entered Patagonian inshore waters to film killer whales (orcas) powering through the shallows to snatch sea lion cubs were gambling on a hunch that the whales would recognize the difference between men and sea lions and leave them alone. The work of film-makers Mike de Gruy, Keith Turner and Paul Atkins, and marine biologists and divers Juan and Diana Lopez, brought a unique phenomenon to the screen: the deliberate self-beaching of whales in pursuit of prey. The film, part of the BBC's *Trials of Life* series shown in 1990, shows the orcas charging groups of sea lions.

Once the target cub has been seized and battered viciously on the shingle, the orca flaps awkwardly around 180° to face the sea, and then heaves itself back into deep water, where several whales will sometimes throw the body of the pup from one to another as if it were a beachball.

For their most dramatic shots, the underwater cameramen had to enter the water with the orcas. One man stayed in the surf, to act as bait. When the whale detected his presence through echo-location, it headed straight towards him, from a distance of several hundred metres. As the gigantic dorsal fin ploughed through the water towards their colleague, two other cameramen dropped into deeper water in the whale's path to take underwater footage of the creature's attacking charge. When the orca was a mere 6m away from the man in the surf, he too dropped beneath the surface and filmed the whale's final approach. All the divers were terrified the first time they carried out this operation. Many experienced Argentinian divers had warned them never to enter the water with the orcas. But the gamble paid off. At the last moment the orca took a close look at the man in the surf, and then turned away, leaving him unharmed.

In the USA, the red wolf, *Canis rufus*, became extinct in the wild in 1980. Wolves throughout the world have suffered severely from human persecution and encroachment on their territories, but naturalists have for some years been publicizing the important role played by wolves in the ecological balance of their environment. In September 1987, the US Fish and Wildlife Service's Red Wolf Recovery Program released four pairs of captive-bred red wolves into the Alligator River National Wildlife Refuge in North Carolina. Two females died, but by 1990 there were nine breeding animals in the refuge.

In 1990 the Program team began preparations to populate a mainland site, in the Great Smoky Mountains National Park in the southern Appalachian Mountains. The breeding animals would come from one of the other refuges. They would be acclimatized to their new terrain by being penned for a breeding season in a large forested area, before being released fully into the Park in the summer of 1991.

Part of the preparations involved calming the fears of local farmers and hunters that the wolves would attack livestock and deplete wild animals hunted for sport. The Program team explained that the red wolf is relatively small, and that it would take rabbits, maybe feral hogs and small or weak white-tailed deer, with beneficial results for the health of the deer herds. The team admitted that wolves straying outside the Park boundaries might be tempted to take farm livestock in the absence of other food. They pointed out, however, that they would be far more likely to remain within the thickly forested cover of the Park.

The breeding animals introduced into the Park would wear special collars equipped with radio-controlled tranquillizer darts that could be activated if there were problems with livestock. In October 1990 the red wolf

Above: Studies of the timber wolf and the moose have revealed how each plays a vital part in maintaining the ecological balance on Isle Royale on Lake Superior. Moose swam across Lake Superior to Isle Royale and timber wolves walked across on the ice one very hard winter. The two species are now part of an ecological balance that keeps both groups healthy by limiting their numbers to what the island can support.

population was up to 125 in captivity and in refuge sites, and prospects look good for a creature that, until recently, was considered to be the world's most endangered mammal.

Large creatures such as tigers, whales and elephants tend to monopolize most of the media and public interest in wildlife, though in terms of total populations they are only the tip of a very large iceberg. Many millions of smaller mammals, reptiles, birds, fishes and invertebrates lead lives every bit as fascinating as those of the wildlife megastars, and are just as rewarding in terms of research. They also suffer the same depredations from the modern industrial world, and in some cases are as much maligned and mistreated as the wolves and sharks further up the size and visibility scale.

In parts of Europe, including Britain, the magpie has a notorious reputation. It is true that magpies will attack and eat other birds, their young and their eggs, as part of their normal behaviour and eating patterns. Many self-professed bird-lovers harbour a particularly virulent dislike for the magpie, claiming that greatly increased magpie numbers over the last two or three decades bode ill for songbird populations.

There is considerable illogic at play here, for the same bird-lovers probably admire birds of prey such as the sparrowhawk, which exacts a far greater toll on its chief prey, birds. The magpie's problem is that it is common, visible and audible. Despite the fears, the evidence does not support the thesis that songbirds are under an increased threat from greater magpie numbers.

Recent research by Stephen Gooch and Tim Birkhead of the Zoology Department of the University of Sheffield, together with Stephen Baillie of the British Trust for Ornithology (BTO), involved a close study of the BTO's Common Bird Census (CBC) and Nest Record Scheme statistics, representing thousands of hours of field work by dedicated amateurs over a period of many years. The records show that magpie numbers have indeed increased in England since 1966 at an annual rate of 4 per cent in rural areas, and over 8 per cent in suburban areas. The statistics also seem to exonerate the magpie from charges of songbird genocide, as there is no sign of any decline in the nesting success of 13 common songbirds, several of which are known magpie prey. Indeed, song thrushes, greenfinches and yellowhammers have had an increased nesting success over the 20 years of the survey, and mostly in the magpie's most common habitats, such as grazing land and scrubland.

The rearers of game for shooting have been the most vociferous denigrators of magpies. In Victorian times they managed to overturn the magpie's reputation as the farmer's friend which ate grain pests, and branded it instead as a thief of eggs and chicks. Research continues, with a BTO and Sheffield University joint effort over 12

Below: The magpie is not nearly as unpleasant a bird as many people would have us believe. Its unenviable reputation as a bandit, a thief and a murderer is due more to the fact that it is relatively common, noisy and visible than to behaviour markedly worse than many other species.

Institute of Zoology have discovered that the queen somehow manages to suppress her subjects' sexual development by her behaviour and presence, although there may also be a chemical element, such as a hormonal suppressant in her urine. Once out of close contact with the queen, a pair of fully grown naked mole rats will begin sexual activity within a few days.

Duncan Brewer

Left: Many unanswered questions still remain concerning the naked mole rat, but recent research has revealed the remarkable ability of the queen of a colony to suppress the sexual development of the other females.

months from spring 1991, to compare blackbird nesting success rates with magpie densities on CBC farmland study plots.

Pandas look cuddly, baby elephants look cute, bald eagles look noble. Naked mole rats are pink, furless and wrinkly, with dots for eyes and big protruding yellow teeth, but despite their rather repulsive appearance they are among the most fascinating of all mammals, with a unique social structure that has more in common with bees or termites than with other rodents.

In recent years much research has been focused on the naked mole rat or sand puppy, and yet there are still unanswered questions. The naked mole rat, a relative of the guinea pig, lives in arid eastern Africa in colonies of 100 or more individuals. These creatures never set foot outside their tunnel systems, which extend for up to 3-4km, and are virtually blind. The long, protruding incisor teeth are used to dig tunnels, carve up the tubers on which the colony lives and, in the case of the soldier caste, to attack any snakes that might enter the tunnels and threaten the community.

The queen naked mole rat is larger than the others, and is the only female member of the colony to mate, bearing a litter of up to a dozen young once every 80 days or so. Apart from the queen and her two or three soldier-consorts, the members of the colony remain sexually immature and infertile, although fully grown, and function as workers and soldiers. Researchers at London's

LEAF-CUTTER ANTS

Researchers are constantly unearthing new facts about the relationships between creatures of different types. Leaf-cutter ants, like most ants, have a complex social structure, with huge ferocious soldiers that guard queen, eggs, and the tiny workers. These workers cultivate gardens deep in the earth, to provide food for both larvae and mature ants. The gardeners work in collaboration with the cutter caste of ants, which cut segments of leaf and bring them back to the nest. A succession of specialized ants of diminishing size cuts the fragments into smaller pieces, pulps them up with a strong digestive fluid, and inserts the pulped fragments into holes in the great balls of fungus nurtured deep in the nest. The tiniest ants of all carry the pulp down narrow passages and fissures in the spongy fungal garden, *planting spores on the pulp and caring for the fungus as it grows to the size where it provides food. Recent research by Dr Donald Feener of the University of Utah and Brian Brown at the University of Alberta revealed the cutter ant's technique for dealing with a parasitic fly that injects its egg into the heads of some ants, but only those with heads larger than 1.6mm in diameter.* Ants in the target group have *learned to work only at night, when the fly is inactive. Ants with smaller heads, which are ignored by the fly, take the day-shift, since they are not at risk.*

THE LIVING DESERT

Deserts occupy almost 20 per cent of the earth's surface. They are found in every continent and may be formed in almost every kind of terrain. Polar deserts, where much of the water remains frozen and inaccessible for most of the year, cover a further 16 per cent of the planet. Deserts form where an average of less than 250mm of rain or snow falls every year. In many, this rainfall is very sporadic: some deserts may receive rain only once or twice a century. Most deserts are barren landscapes with sparse vegetation, yet the sporadic rains produce a great flowering of the deserts, which feed some 2 per cent of the world's population and have a thriving wildlife.

The adaptations of desert animals are many and varied. Deserts the world over have developed surprisingly similar wildlife — there are web-footed geckos in Africa and Australia, fringe-footed lizards in America, Africa and Australia, sidewinder snakes in the American south-west, the Sahara and the Namib, large flightless birds such as ostriches, rheas and emus in Africa, South America and Australia respectively, and predatory dogs such as the coyote and jackal, once matched by the Australian thylacine or Tasmanian wolf.

At first sight, the desert may appear devoid of life. Many of the animals that live there avoid the heat of the day, sheltering in underground burrows and rock crevices or hiding under stones. Even cold-blooded lizards and snakes, which need warmth in order to become active, bask in the sun in the early morning, hunt for a short time, then retreat until the cool of late afternoon.

In sandy deserts, many animals both shelter and hunt beneath the sand. Many desert lizards, and some desert spiders, have fringes of bristles or hard skin along their toes that act as both sand-shoes and shovels. Some can literally dive into hot sand if danger threatens, aided by shovel-shaped snouts. Valves on their nostrils close to prevent the entry of sand, and a transparent disc in their eyelids enables them to see with their eyes closed, while protecting them from the sand.

Desert animals face three major problems: extremes of temperature both daily and seasonally, shortage of water and shortage of food. In the world's hot deserts, high temperatures by day, cold at night and limited water all require animals to be specially adapted. Small animals have a large surface area from which to radiate heat away from their bodies, but this makes them more susceptible to water loss. Stores of body fat, which provide food in times of shortage but also act as insulating layers, trapping the animal's body heat, are often localized: the camel confines most of its fat to its hump, while many species of desert lizards and mice store it in fat tails. The long, slender

Right: This regal horned lizard from Arizona blends almost imperceptibly into its background of sharp stones. Camouflage is its main form of defence against predators.

Below: The ostrich is unable to fly but is highly adapted for running and can reach speeds of over 70km/h. Speed is the bird's method of escaping from danger, and also allows it to range widely in search of food.

legs of gazelles and desert antelopes hold their bodies well clear of the hot ground and allow air to circulate, carrying away the heat.

One of the commonest ways of cooling is to sweat or pant, but this causes moisture loss. Kangaroos lick their forearms — heat is lost as the moisture evaporates. Desert tortoises dribble urine over their hind legs and saliva over their heads, necks and front legs for cooling. Camels and ostriches conserve moisture by allowing their body temperature to rise to an almost lethal level before starting to sweat or pant.

Walking on a hot surface presents problems. Many desert lizards 'dance' while standing still, raising diagonally opposite feet off the ground at short intervals. Sidewinders appear to roll across the desert with only three small areas of their bodies touching the ground at any one time.

One of the major sources of water in deserts is the dew that forms as a result of the steep temperature drop during the night. Many desert animals feed in the early morning, taking in dew with the plants they feed on. Small insects such as ants can drink direct from the dewdrops. Some coastal deserts, such as the Namib of southern Africa, the Atacama of South America and the Baja Desert of California, are often bathed in sea fog, and some of the darkling beetles have grooves running along their wing cases. During fog, they stand on their heads with their abdomens tilted skywards, so that the moisture condensing on their bodies runs down to their mouths.

Most desert animals obtain their water from food — from succulent desert plants, or from the bodies of other animals: the dorcas gazelle is said never to drink. Other creatures range widely in search of water — sandgrouse fly 80km or more, and have an unusual adaptation for carrying water to their chicks: the belly feathers soak up water, which the young then suck, usually from the male bird.

Desert tortoises, camels, wild asses and ostriches can survive the loss of up to one-third of their body weight of water, whereas humans die if they lose a mere one-eighth. The ostrich and camel can replace such large volumes of water in a single drinking session. Desert tortoises and some desert frogs and toads store water in a greatly enlarged urinary bladder.

The use of underground burrows during the hottest time of day saves a lot of water, as well as being cooler. The kangaroo rat of western American deserts plugs the entrance to its burrow with earth while it shelters. Heat from its body is absorbed by the cool burrow walls, and moisture from the burrow is absorbed by the rat. As the rat breathes out, it makes the air in the burrow very moist, which reduces evaporation, until the humidity in the burrow may be five times greater than in the air outside. Kangaroo rats can survive in deserts where the midday temperature reaches 60°C.

Shortage of food is a perennial problem for animals in the hottest and most arid of deserts, and a seasonal problem for those of high mountains, temperate and polar deserts. Some animals store fat in their bodies, while others hoard seeds, hay and other plant material in burrows or underground caches. Harvester ants and termites may remove as much as one-third of the total desert production of plant material. The honeypot ants of the USA store nectar in the distended abdomens of certain worker ants as a reserve in times of drought.

The sparse vegetation cover and water supplies of deserts encourage the nomadic lifestyles of gazelles and antelopes, zebras and wild asses, kangaroos and the large ostriches, emus and rheas. Vultures roam over hundreds of kilometres, effortlessly riding the air currents on their broad wings. But the greatest desert nomads are the locusts, whose swarms can contain up to 10 billion individuals. They can travel up to 3000km in a season, and consume their own body weight of plant material every day — proof of the deserts' ability to support life.

The survival of desert life depends on the intimate inter-relationship between the animals and plants and the erratic climate, the fine tuning of breeding cycles and feeding patterns, and the subtle adaptations that have evolved over many millions of years in the deserts of the world.

Jill Bailey

Left: Underground burrows remain cooler than the surface. In the Americas small birds such as this elf owl shelter from the sun in a cactus.

Overleaf: Desert terrain can offer some of the world's most spectacular natural scenery. This is the White Desert in Egypt, north of the Farafra oasis.

Below: The camel's nose is adapted to conserve water. As the dry air enters, moisture in the nose evaporates and cools the air being breathed out.

ANIMALS ON ICE

Above: One of the most spectacular feats of migration is that of the Arctic tern. Each year this bird flies from the Arctic to Antarctic.

Right: Arctic wolves hunt cooperatively for large animals such as musk oxen and caribou, and individually for smaller prey such as Arctic hares, birds and lemmings.

Far right: The ice fish has developed an 'antifreeze' system that enables it to avoid freezing completely and stay active, swimming and feeding under the sea ice.

The Antarctic interior is the coldest place on the planet. For a few heady hours in mid-summer the air temperature may rise to −21°C, but within weeks it can drop 30°, 40° or even 50° to a level that few living organisms can survive. The land surface is buried beneath a sheet of ice 2000m thick, covered by a blanket of snow that never melts. In winter the sun never rises above the bleak horizon, so the continent is shrouded in permanent darkness.

The barren interior of Antarctica is no place for animals to live. They are scattered around the edge of the continent, on coastal strips and islands that are free of permanent ice. Beyond lies the Southern Ocean, isolating them from the rest of the world. Since the only way to reach Antarctica is by sea, which is also the only source of food, virtually all the creatures that live in the region are marine animals, including six different species of seal, twelve species of whale and six species of penguin, as well as vast numbers of other seabirds.

At the other end of the world, the Arctic is quite different. Instead of a frozen continent surrounded by ocean, the Arctic is a frozen ocean surrounded by the continents of North America, Europe and northern Asia. The ice sheets are as cold and barren as those of Antarctica, but the polar fringes, where most of the animals live, are at the northern limits of large landmasses: Scandinavia, Siberia, Alaska and Canada. So the Arctic is not cut off like the Antarctic. Land animals can come and go as they please, moving north from the great forests across the boggy half-frozen tundra to the ice edge itself. Some of them have stayed.

But why should animals leave the shelter of the forests to venture into the bleak expanses of the north? The reason is that,

contrary to appearances, the polar fringes are incredibly rich feeding grounds. Throughout the winter they are clamped down under a dead weight of ice and shrouded in permanent darkness, but in spring the sun comes out, the snows melt, the sea ice cracks up and all the polar plant life bursts into bloom. Within weeks the Arctic lands are a mass of blossom as the specially adapted plants make the most of the short summer.

As the land blooms, so do the seas. The cold polar oceans hold more dissolved carbon dioxide and oxygen than warm waters, and are particularly rich in minerals scoured up from the bottom by ocean currents. As a result they are immensely fertile, providing ideal growing conditions for the floating

garden of microscopic algae known as the phytoplankton.

When the sea ice melts in spring the water is suddenly flooded with 24-hour sunlight; the phytoplankton explodes into an orgy of growth and reproduction, and before long the sea is thick with plant life. The blooming algae attracts a host of tiny floating animals — the zooplankton — and the whole teeming mass provides a feast for the flourishing populations of fish, crustaceans, molluscs and the animals that prey on them.

In the summer, then, the polar fringes offer rich pickings, but the animals that exploit them have to find ways of surviving the terrible winter months. Some creatures have adapted to the extreme cold in a

Above: In winter, the Antarctic krill sink below the near-freezing surface of the water into the ocean depths, down to 2000m or more. Here the temperature is stable and the krill can survive in a state of semi-dormancy.

surprising variety of ways. Others find shelter, and either keep active or lie dormant until they are roused by the spring sun. Many simply leave, migrating to warmer regions and returning with the thaw.

The polar bear is the best adapted of all land mammals to the cold. Not only is it equipped with a heavy coat of dense underfur overlaid with long guard hairs, but it also has a thick layer of fat which protects it from the cold and helps to keep it afloat when swimming in the Arctic seas to look for food.

Emperor penguins manage to breed on the sea ice during the Antarctic winter, the aim being to rear the chick to the point where it can feed itself when the sea ice melts. This means that the egg has to be incubated during the coldest part of the winter, which is a full-time job; it cannot be exposed to the savage cold for more than a few seconds or the chick will die.

Incubation is the male's responsibility. Once the female has produced the egg she passes it to him and makes her way back to the sea to feed. He places the egg on his foot, covers it with a fold of his belly and sits tight without eating for 60 days or so, enduring the worst that the winter can throw at him. The incubating males usually huddle together to conserve warmth, but otherwise they have no protection except their own body insulation, which dwindles week by week as the fat resources are used

up. They do have one other trick, though. With any warm-blooded animal the main priority is to maintain the temperature of the body core, but as blood flows out to the extremities it tends to drain away some of this heat. In the penguin this is minimized by a heat-exchanger system in each limb. The arteries carrying the outgoing warm blood flow very close to the veins carrying the returning cool blood. Consequently the heat passes straight into the returning blood flow and is carried back to the body core. The penguin's feet and flippers stay relatively cold — but it is used to that.

For many other creatures, surviving the cold means a thick layer of fat, feathers or fur combined with some form of shelter from the lethally low winter air temperatures. The Weddell seal, for example, stays in the water beneath the Antarctic sea ice, where the temperature never drops much below freezing point. The seal's insulating fat layer enables it to cope with this easily, but it may have to bite holes through the ice in order to breathe. Weddell seals often congregate in places where pressure has forced the ice into hummocks, creating sheltered ice caverns above the water level.

Other polar animals seem to manage without special adaptations of any kind. Some Arctic wolves follow the caribou herds on their migrations, so they miss the worst of the winter, but others living in the High

Right: Following well-marked trails, herds of 25,000–50,000 caribou may cover distances of over 500km to take advantage of the spring grass on the tundra. Some females calve on the march, although most bear their calves on the summer pastures where the good grazing enables them to produce plenty of milk.

Arctic are resident all year round. Each pack has an enormous territory where the wolves hunt cooperatively for prey.

During the summer prey is easily come by, but in winter the wolves have a struggle to survive. They manage because they are able to go for days without eating, then gorge themselves when they make a kill. Each wolf may eat up to 45kg of meat at a sitting, wasting nothing and burying any surplus in the frozen ground. If the pack concentrates on tracking large prey such as musk oxen there is a good chance that it will make at least one big kill a week, and this will see the wolves through to the spring when the sun reappears, the flowers bloom and the migrants return.

Some small creatures such as insects and spiders are cold-blooded, with no internal means of keeping themselves warm, so cannot stay active. Many Arctic insects can operate at temperatures close to freezing, but below this they become sluggish and seize up. In temperate climates such animals hibernate, lying dormant until the spring, but any animal that does this in the polar winter is liable to freeze solid. Normally, freezing is fatal to organic cells.

The water in them turns to ice, and the ice crystals rupture the cell walls and destroy them; the results are familiar to any gardener who has seen a spring flowerbed reduced to brown mush by a late frost. The average insect would finish up in the same state if it became cold enough.

One method that animals have evolved to deal with this problem is supercooling: the development of a natural 'antifreeze' in the body fluids that lowers their freezing point. This works well up to a point, but so extreme is the cold of the Arctic winter that most Arctic insects have had to find ways of limiting the damage caused by the development of ice crystals within their bodies.

They do this by allowing the fluids surrounding their body cells to freeze in a controlled fashion, while the cells themselves are protected. Special proteins actually encourage the formation of many small ice crystals, which are kept separate by the 'antifreeze'. The small ice crystals do no harm, and in their supercooled state the cells — and therefore the organs — of the insect can survive without oxygen until the temperature rises again. Using this system, the caterpillar of the moth *Gynaephora*

Above: Humpback whales belong to the suborder of baleen whales that, in place of teeth, have a system of horny plates called baleen, used to filter the tiny marine organisms that form the main part of their diet. They consume vast quantities of planktonic creatures such as krill during intensive feeding sessions.

Above: Lemmings normally stay on their summer feeding grounds in the Arctic throughout the winter, remaining active under the insulating snow.

groenlandica can survive being frozen at temperatures down to -50°C for 10 months or more in the High Arctic.

Recently a salamander has been found using a similar mechanism to survive freezing on the tundra of Arctic Siberia; it floods its vital organs with a glucose-based antifreeze and allows small ice crystals to form throughout the rest of its body. With up to 65 per cent of its body water converted to ice, the salamander can survive temperatures down to -35°C in its underground refuge, and emerge in spring none the worse for its experience.

Fishes never have to endure such low temperatures, unless they are actually frozen into the sea ice. Despite this, they still have a problem. The body fluids of the average fish have a higher freezing point than seawater. If the fish swims into a patch of water that is on the point of freezing, it will turn into ice itself.

To prevent this, polar fishes such as the Antarctic ice fish have developed an antifreeze similar to that of polar insects. As long as the ice fish stays clear of very cold ice it can avoid freezing. But the system only works up to a certain point; if the fish were to stay in close contact with the ice for too long its body temperature would fall below the critical point and it would freeze uncontrollably — and fatally.

Finally, what of the creatures that choose to escape the polar winter? The most spectacular migration is that of the Arctic tern, a delicate-looking seabird with a taste for small fish and crustaceans which it plucks from the ocean surface with its slender red bill. Such prey teems in the plankton-rich polar oceans in summer, but dwindles as winter sets in. So, having reared its young on the summer abundance of the Arctic Ocean, the Arctic tern takes the obvious but astounding course and flies south, all the

Right: The emperor penguin breeds in the coldest conditions endured by any bird. Its feathers are tiny, scale-like and close-packed to prevent water from touching the bird's skin. Before breeding, the male accumulates fat reserves, 40 per cent of which may be lost during the incubation of the egg.

way to Antarctica: a distance of some 18,000km. By the time it arrives the sea ice is melting and the plankton is blooming. For the Arctic tern it is a home from home, with food in plenty and 24-hour daylight — indeed, it enjoys more daylight in its life than any other living creature.

The Arctic tern migrates across the globe, but one of its food sources the Antarctic krill, migrates downwards into the ocean depths. These planktonic shrimp-like creatures are probably the most abundant animals on the planet, forming vast swarms in the Southern Ocean which can extend for hundreds of kilometres. The total weight of Antarctic krill is estimated to be at least 650 million tonnes, or more than the weight of the entire human race. In Antarctica, krill are the main food of the great whales, many seals, penguins, albatrosses and other seabirds; indeed, the whole ecology of the continent depends on them.

In winter, krill become much harder to find as their main food, the phytoplankton, dies off. During this lean period the krill-feeders have a problem. Smaller animals such as fish and seabirds can make do with what they find, but the great whales such as the humpback and the blue whale can rarely find enough to satisfy their immense appetites — a blue whale may engulf 3 tonnes of krill in a single feeding session. To survive, the whales that spend the summer in Antarctic waters regularly migrate north to plankton-rich areas off the coasts of South America, Africa and Australia, breeding in the warm waters and returning south in the summer.

In the Arctic, land mammals make similar migrations. Most conspicuous are the caribou, which trek north from the forests of Canada and Alaska to their summer grazing areas in the High Arctic — the islands in the far north.

The larger groups are often accompanied by 'resident' packs of wolves that pick off

the old and sick animals, ultimately doing the herds a service by culling the weaklings. Far more of a problem are the clouds of bloodsucking mosquitoes that hatch from the tundra pools at the beginning of summer, driving the caribou up into the mountain foothills where the grazing is not so good. By early September most of the nutritious herbage has gone, and as the first snows begin to fall the caribou make their way south again, feeding on the lichens that will sustain them until the next year's great trek north.

At first sight bleak and inhospitable, the polar regions are in fact rich in unusual mammals, birds and insects. Forced into remarkable strategies and feats of endurance to overcome the problems of terrible cold, these creatures are among the most fascinating of the earth's wildlife.

John Woodward

Above: The Weddell seal bears its young in a habitat of stable sea ice. The pups grow quickly, tripling their weight in four to six weeks, and laying down sufficient fat to protect them when the ice which forms their homes breaks up.

CREATURES OF THE DEEP

The deep oceans cover three-quarters of our planet's surface, yet they remain the last great unknown area of the earth. Much of our knowledge about the animals that live there is from dead or dying specimens brought up in trawls or caught on baited hooks. It is almost impossible to study live specimens, since creatures of the deep oceans are so specialized and well adapted to their environment that they quickly die at sea level.

The deep oceans provide a habitat for a vast number of species of fish and other creatures, yet the conditions of life in the deep sea are inhospitable in the extreme. On average, the oceans are about 4km deep. Since the pressure increases by the equivalent of the atmosphere above us for every 10m of water, the pressure on the ocean floor is usually 400 times greater than we experience on land.

Living in the deep sea is like being at the bottom of a well, with very little light filtering down from above, even on the brightest day. The lack of light also means that food is a problem, since the microscopic green plants that live in the sea can obtain enough sunlight to make food only down to about 150m, and most animals depend on plants as their source of food.

So what sort of creatures manage to survive in the depths of such an uncompromising marine environment? Large animals, such as giant squid with eyes the size of dinner plates, have been reported to live in the deep oceans, but few have been caught in recent years. Some deep-sea sharks are over a metre long. There must be migrating

Right: The angler fish is a master of camouflage. It lurks in the darkened waters waiting for its prey to pass by. Above its mouth a long, thin, rod-like protrusion with a flap of skin on the tip is used to guide prey through its huge jaws.

Above: Many creatures living more than 1km underwater produce their own light from special light organs (photophores). We do not know for certain whether it is dark in the sea with only occasional flashes or whether there are lights flashing all the time.

eels swimming through the deep oceans, but they are never caught. Most of the ferocious-looking fishes from the deep oceans are in fact only a few centimetres long, and this is probably due to the chronic shortage of food.

Photographic traps where a dead fish is used as bait and photographed at intervals show that in a short time it is covered with scavenging animals of various types, such

as brittle stars or hagfish. Because there is a shortage of plant material for food, creatures in the ocean are dependent on a food source that has to drift down as dead animals or 'marine snow' from the surface waters to the depths of the seas. It is not surprising that the animals are not very numerous and mostly quite small.

The only daylight in the sea comes from directly above. It is a deep, clear, ultramarine blue because pure water is more transparent to blue light than to light of the other colours of the spectrum. At noon on the brightest days in the clearest oceans, there is enough daylight for the most sensitive animals to see down to about 1km. Deep-sea fish, however, are able to see in light too dim for human eyes. Rhodopsin, the light-sensitive pigment that animals use to harness light rays, is present in these animals in much greater amounts than in human eyes, and they are particularly sensitive to the blue colour of daylight that penetrates down to them. Many deep-sea fish have adapted in other ways to their environment; some have a tapetum or reflective lining at the back of the eye, like certain nocturnal land animals. Light that is not absorbed by the light-sensitive pigment

Right: The black swallower fish lives in the deepest parts of the oceans, up to 3km below the surface. It has a series of feeler stalks that pick up the vibrations of passing prey such as this hatchet fish.

in its passage through the eye the first time is reflected back by the tapetum for a second chance of absorption.

At depths greater than 1km it would be perpetually dark if it were not for the lights produced by the creatures themselves. This bioluminescence is produced by all kinds of animals, from the truly microscopic to jellyfish of many different kinds, prawns, octopuses, cuttlefish and fish. The lights appear to serve many different purposes, although it is impossible to be sure of the details because of the difficulties of observing the creatures in their natural environment.

Some guesses about the function of the lights may not be too wide of the mark. For example, each species of lantern fish has its own pattern of lights along its sides. It seems most likely that these are used as recognition signals, especially as in some species the males and females have different patterns. Sometimes the lights flash in regular rhythms, and it is probable that they are used for various types of signals — perhaps advertising for the opposite sex, as fireflies do on land.

It appears that lights play a part in the bizarre sex life of the deep-sea angler fish. The male and female are so different that it is difficult to believe they belong to the same species. She is round and rather squat and rests on the bottom with a luminous lure dangling close to her mouth. He is much smaller and rather more like an ordinary fish, except that he has enormous 'nostrils' and his eyes are tube-shaped and point forward. She spends her time on the sea bed waiting for animals the right size for eating to swim within range of her large mouth. He has only one mission in life, which is to find a female. It is likely that he is first alerted to the presence of a female by her scent, and when he has got sufficiently near, homes in on her luminous lure.

One use for bioluminescence that is almost certainly of major importance is,

Above: Very few species of shark are dangerous to humans. Most, like this cat shark, live close to the ocean bed and feed on small fish and plankton.

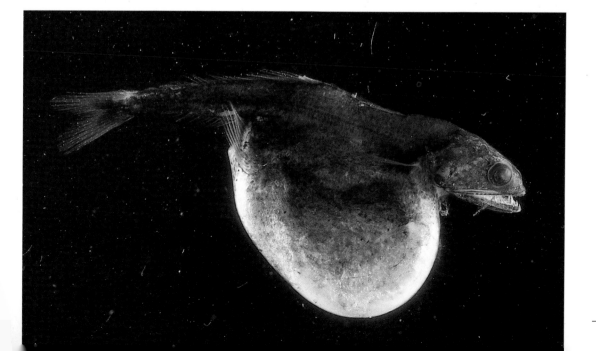

Left: Although its mouth is small, the black swallower's jaw can unhinge, allowing it to consume prey much larger than itself.

47

paradoxically, camouflage. Many fish living in the top 1km of the ocean, where some daylight penetrates, have eyes that point directly upwards, probably to allow them to see their prey silhouetted against the daylight that comes down from above. It is impossible for the prey animals to use ordinary colours and patterns to conceal themselves from the watchers below, as they will always show up as a dark silhouette. The solution adopted by many unrelated animals like squid, prawns and fish is to arrange downward-pointing lights along their belly that are the same blue colour as the daylight in the sea, and that can also be adjusted in brightness. Prawns even have a special light organ — the organ of Pesta — which can be swivelled to point directly downwards, whatever position the prawn takes up in the water. Below about 100m, fish with belly-light camouflage become rare, and indeed bioluminescence is much less common in deeper waters.

Because the light in the deep oceans is blue, most bioluminescent animals use blue light, especially for camouflage. As always in nature, though, there are some creatures that break the rules. One of these is the deep-sea fish *Malacosteus*. This has a photophore (a light-making organ) beneath the eye that produces red light. Research on the visual pigments in its eye shows that it is also capable of detecting red light, which is probably invisible to most other deep-sea creatures. This is an exceptionally useful secret weapon, with the photophore acting as a kind of searchlight to pick up any prey animal which is red in colour and reflects back the light (perhaps a prawn), without the prawn even being aware that it is under surveillance. In the absence of naturally occurring red light in the ocean, red animals otherwise look black and are exceptionally difficult to find, unless the predator is directly below them and looking upwards.

So how have humans been able to explore this deep, dark and inhospitable world? Our knowledge of life in shallow water — down to 50m or so — has been revolutionized by scuba equipment, which makes it possible and relatively cheap to observe fish and other creatures directly in their own element. The difficulty of going deeper than this by conventional scuba is that the great pressure of the water causes ordinary gases in the air like nitrogen and oxygen to become poisonous. By substituting helium for nitrogen and reducing the amount of oxygen in the diver's breathing mixture, it is possible (at great expense) to free dive to a depth of around 300m.

Probing into the really deep parts of the ocean is similar to space exploration. For deeper diving, individual armoured diving suits such as 'Jim' and 'Wasp' have been tried, but these cost a small fortune to launch and recover. Most of the information we have about the deep oceans has been gathered by manned submersibles, which give the opportunity to observe while keeping the pressure inside the vessel close to that at the surface.

It was a manned submersible, for example, that made the exciting discovery of a

completely new environment for animals in the rifts of the ocean floor. These are long volcanic rifts in the sea bed that mark the junction between the continental plates. Molten volcanic rock comes near to the surface where the plates meet and water seeping down from above is heated to well over boiling point, but because of the enormous pressure it does not bubble but is expelled into the ocean above in plumes of dark sulphide-stained water called hot smokers. So hot is the water that it melted the first remotely controlled temperature probes that were inserted into it from the submersible *Alvin*. Clustered around these volcanic rifts is a unique collection of animals whose existence was not even suspected until a few years ago. There are giant clams and white squat lobsters and crabs and bacteria large enough to be seen with the naked eye. The bacteria are the largest known on earth, but they have another unique characteristic — they appear to be able to live in water so hot that it would hard-boil an egg. The most obviously spectacular of all the creatures that live around the volcanic rifts are the giant tube worms which stand higher than a man and are crowned at the top with a feather-like plume. They contain so much haemoglobin (the red substance in human blood) that the laboratories on the research ships that study them smell like butchers' shops filled with raw meat.

In the deep ocean rifts volcanic heat is used by the bacteria to make food. The heat forms sulphides that release energy in the presence of oxygen from the surrounding seawater, and the energy is harnessed to make organic materials. The bacteria then form an important food source for the other animals in the ocean depths.

It was also submersibles that first recorded the almost continuous pattern of flashing lights from deep-sea creatures. It is impossible to know for sure, however, whether they are the creatures' response to the submersibles' own bright lights intruding on their environment.

Despite the remarkable discoveries made by submersibles in the deep oceans, this work has now been discontinued because many governments feel that the enormous expense cannot currently be justified. Just as space is not yet ready to give up its secrets, it seems that it will be many years before the mysterious aquatic environment of the deep sea is fully explored and understood.

John Lythgoe

Left: Small pressurized submersibles such as *Alvin* are the only way scientists have of reaching the deepest parts of the oceans, but using them is dangerous. The decompression process after the dive must be carefully controlled and can last for several days.

Below: The hatchet fish (bottom) is one of the most common types of fish found in the deep oceans. The long tail resembles the handle of a hatchet and the large thin body resembles the blade. It has evolved a vertical mouth to cover as large a surface area of its face as possible. The lantern fish (top) gives off yellow, blue and green light signals for communicating.

MATING

The most important moment in an animal's life is when it gives birth to the next generation. But before this can happen, male and female must come together to mate. During mating, the male is usually the donor animal, the female the recipient. Both animals produce special sex cells, the sperm and eggs, which contain the code for all the animal's distinctive characteristics. Mating is the way in which the male's sperm is brought into contact with the female's eggs for fertilization. Without the mixing of the genetic material from different animals that occurs through mating, the great diversity of animals in the world today would not have evolved.

Many animals that live underwater, especially sedentary marine animals, do not

Below: The act of mating in birds is always brief. In the case of species such as the chinstrap penguin, it may also demand feats of quite considerable agility to ensure that the male's sperm is successfully transferred.

bother to mate in the accepted sense. They simply release eggs and swimming sperm into the water, and leave them to find each other. This can be an extremely wasteful process since many eggs and sperm will fail to pair up, or will be eaten by predators. To ensure a greater success rate, there needs to be a means of releasing the eggs and sperm at the same time in the same place. This is usually done by chemical signals. In

spawning mussels, for example, when the first mussel releases its sperm, it also releases a chemical that diffuses through the water and causes all the other mussels in the area to release their eggs or sperm. In this great cocktail of eggs and sperm, sex cells from different mussels mingle and fuse, giving rise to new variation in the next generation. Over vast areas of the Great Barrier Reef in Australia almost all the species of coral spawn simultaneously in such profusion that the sea turns pink.

Larger animals such as frogs, toads and most species of fish also shed their eggs and sperm into the water. But there is usually some process of courtship that attracts pairs of animals to each other and excites them so that they simultaneously release their eggs and sperm. Male frogs clasp females under the armpits and wriggle their bodies

Above: When lions copulate, a good deal of roaring precedes and accompanies the process. The male will stay close to the female for a few days afterwards to ward off potential rivals and ensure that she does not attempt to mate with any of them.

Above: The female praying mantis sometimes bites off the male's head while they are still in the act of copulating. She subsequently eats her partner and thus gains valuable extra protein to pass on to her eggs.

Right: A number of tiny male deep-sea angler fish are attracted to the much larger female by her special chemical secretions. They latch on to her with their teeth and gradually become fused to her until, as their organs shrivel away, all that remains is a sperm sac. This is activated by the female to fertilize her eggs at spawning time.

against them, while male fish will often prod the females' bellies to persuade them to release the eggs, perhaps into a nest where they cannot easily drift away before they have had a chance to be fertilized.

External fertilization is not an option for terrestrial animals because eggs and sperm need moisture to survive. Many of them have special organs with which to inject the sperm directly into the female's body. This reduces wastage, and allows more energy to be devoted to producing food for the developing eggs. Fewer eggs need to be produced, since more will survive, resulting in a further saving in energy. Since the eggs are fertilized inside the female's body, they can be retained there after fertilization, so that the embryos can develop in a warm, stable environment until they are large enough to have a better chance of survival in the outside world.

Very few immobile animals use internal fertilization. The barnacle is, however, a notable exception. For its size, the barnacle has the longest penis in the animal kingdom, but even so, it can mate only with its closest neighbours.

Insects, reptiles, birds, mammals and even a few species of fish use internal fertilization, and so do spiders, squid and octopuses, but they go about it in many different ways. Sometimes the male will keep possession of his female until she is ready to lay her eggs.

Male dragonflies clasp the females behind the head and fly around with them. This ensures that no other male has the chance to fertilize the eggs. Even large mammals such as lions and tigers will remain with their mates for a few days after mating. Others, such as wild dogs and the males of many birds, even stay and help to rear the young.

Eggs and sperm do not have to be released at the same time. Many animals, ranging from bees to bats, have means of storing sperm. A queen bee obtains enough sperm on her mating flight to fertilize all the eggs she needs to sustain the new bee colony for many years.

In some species, the release of ripe eggs is triggered by the mating act itself, which may require rather prolonged and vigorous mating. This is carried to an extreme in dogs, which often remain in a tail to tail tie after mating. Once the male's penis has entered the female, a powerful muscle contraction prevents him from withdrawing it, sometimes for several hours. Dogs and some other mammals that need to mate for long periods have a supportive bone inside the penis. An alternative to prolonged mating is frequent mating. Lions and tigers may mate over 80 times a day. The record is held by Shaw's jird, a desert jumping mouse, which has

been recorded copulating no fewer than 224 times in two hours.

Some animals are so heavily armoured that mating presents special problems. Male crabs cannot mate until the female moults her shell, when for a short time her body will be soft and pliable. The male crab will often cling to the back of his mate for days, waiting for her to moult. Classic examples of the need for extreme care are porcupines and hedgehogs, where the female flattens her spines as the male mounts her. The egg-laying echidnas of Australia and New Guinea take no such chances — they mate spineless belly to spineless belly.

An even greater hazard is faced by some carnivorous invertebrates. In many species of spiders, the males are much smaller than the females. By a delicate and elaborate courtship ritual of web-vibrating and visual signals, the male informs the female that he is a mate, not a meal. In some species, it is expedient for the male to offer the female a present of a silk-wrapped fly, so that he can nip in and fertilize her while she is distracted by eating it. Even so, some male spiders get eaten before, or even after, they mate.

A different form of internal fertilization occurs in many invertebrates, and in some newts. The male parcels his sperm into a small packet called a spermatophore. The male scorpion engages the female in what looks rather like a dance, grasping her claws in his and guiding her over the spermatophore he has just deposited on the ground until she takes it up into her cloaca.

In a few rare instances, unusual relationships have evolved between quite different species. The bitterling, a small fish, injects her eggs into the mantle cavity of a freshwater mussel, having first gently stroked it to persuade it to open its shell. The male's sperm are drawn in with the mussel's breathing currents. The eggs are fertilized inside the mussel, and the fish larvae develop there until large enough to survive outside. When they leave on the mussel's outgoing water currents, the mussel's own larvae attach to them as parasites, and are thus dispersed.

Jill Bailey

Left: Slugs are hermaphrodites, and when mating they circle each other, both flapping their mantles until they have generated a globule of slime. They extend their sexual organs and writhe in the slime, wrapping themselves around one another until they have exchanged sperm.

Below: The male octopus uses seven arms to arouse the female and the eighth to insert his spermatophore inside her. This arm sometimes breaks off, and for many years was thought to be a parasitic worm occasionally found in female octopuses.

HUNTING

Above: Tiger sharks are named for the barred markings along their sides. Among the most aggressive members of the shark family, their jaws are lined with rows of fearsome serrated teeth with which they tear into the flesh of their prey.

Right: In spite of its enormous size, the grizzly bear is both quick on its feet and extremely agile. It also has lightning-fast reactions, which it needs when fishing for salmon. It catches its prey in its teeth or claws and takes it ashore before carefully stripping off the flesh from either side, leaving the head, tail and bones.

Throughout the ages, large powerful hunting animals have captured the imagination of the human race. Ancient buildings and tombs are adorned with images and sculptures of lions, eagles and wolves. Many an adventure film has featured a shark or crocodile as the villain. But there are other hunters — much smaller, but nonetheless impressive — such as the praying mantids, scorpions and hunting spiders, as well as the more fearsome lizards, many of which are the giant-killers of their own world. Claws, sharp teeth and venomous bites and stings are commonplace, but some predators have evolved unusual weapons: the archerfish shoots down insects from overhanging branches by firing a jet of water at them; mantis shrimps stun their victims with the sound from the snapping of their huge claws; and octopus, squid and cuttlefish use tentacles armed with suckers to seize their prey.

Perhaps the most effective hunters use ambush. For this technique they need good camouflage, some of them even mimicking leaves, stones and other inanimate objects. Some predators bury themselves in sand or mud, with only their eyes showing. Many desert snakes hide in the sand, and crocodiles and alligators have eyes and eardrums on the tops of their heads, so that the rest of their bodies can remain hidden just below the water surface as they wait for animals to come to the shore to drink.

Instead of passively waiting for prey to pass within reach, a few predators lure prey towards them. The snapping turtle uses a worm-like lure, actually in the floor of its mouth, to tempt unwary fish to swim right between its jaws. There are lures in the insect world, too. Fireflies flash at night to attract mates, each species having its own distinctive pattern of flashes. But there is

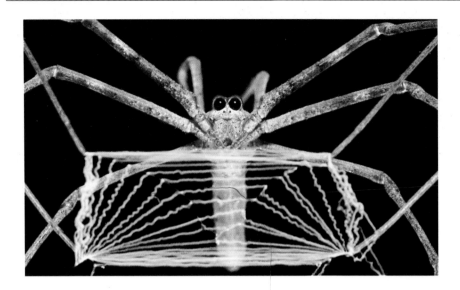

Above: As its name suggests, the net-casting spider is a rather more active hunter than many of its relatives. It spins a small web of crinkled silk and hangs upside-down, dangling the web from its two long front legs. When an appropriate prey scuttles across the ground below, the spider flings the web over it. The covered insect struggles and quickly becomes fatally entangled.

The bolas spider (named after a weapon consisting of a rope with two or more stones attached, thrown by hunters in South America to entangle and bring down birds and other animals) is much more active. It preys on night-flying moths, which it attracts by emitting a scent similar to that of the female moth. The spider spins a sticky ball of silk on a long thread which it twirls round and round like a bolas until it hits a moth flying to investigate the scent.

Despite its formidable name, the ant-lion is a small insect, the larva of a lacewing fly. It lives in sandy areas, where it excavates a conical pit and hides itself in the centre, waiting for passing ants to fall in — hence its name. If the ant looks like escaping, the ant-lion bombards it with sand to knock it back into the pit.

The largest traps in the animal world are the great moving traps of the baleen or whalebone whales, whose mouths contain giant filters — fringed plates of whalebone. The whales gulp in huge mouthfuls of shrimps and other tiny marine creatures, then squeeze the water out through these sieves.

One of the most unusual underwater traps is the bubble net of the humpback whale. The whale circles below a shoal of krill and spirals slowly to the surface, emitting bubbles of air that encircle the prey, keeping them concentrated together until the whale eventually lunges vertically through them, its mouth wide open.

one firefly that emits the flash pattern of the female from another species. When the unsuspecting males approach, the females seize and devour them.

The setting of traps requires slightly more effort. The most familiar examples are the webs of spiders, whose sticky threads entangle any insect that flies or crawls into them. Linking the sticky threads are non-sticky ones which the spider uses to travel around its web. Usually it rests one foot on the web to pick up any vibrations caused by the struggles of prey. Some spiders do not create such a carefully structured web, but instead spin a large sticky sheet to trap crickets and other fast-flying insects. A few tropical spiders form vast communal sheet webs in tiered columns several metres high.

Right and far right: The chameleon is a master of disguise — in the second picture the animal is already beginning to turn darker and blend with the background — but this is not its only talent. It can shoot out its tongue with lightning speed and accuracy to capture an unsuspecting insect on its sticky tip. The tongue may be well over 10cm long.

Left: Flesh-eaters have preyed on grass-eaters for more than 60 million years. Although not as fast as some hunting species like the cheetah, the lioness is nevertheless far too quick for the buffalo. Even so, the hunt does not always go her way — she has been wounded during the chase.

Most of the larger predators stalk or chase their prey. It is exciting to watch a lioness or a tiger stalking, the body held close to the ground, the head stretched out, ears flattened for better concealment, the rippling muscles suggesting immense power. Polar bears adopt a similar posture. Unless an ambush is very successful, a predator will require a good turn of speed, or it may need to cooperate with others to capture its prey. The cheetah holds the animal speed record, running at up to 100km/h, although it can keep up this pace for only a short distance. Speed is important in the air, too. Falcons, which catch other birds on the wing, usually have narrow curved and pointed wings for high speed and good manoeuvrability. The peregrine falcon swoops down on its prey from a great height, reaching speeds of up to 180km/h.

An alternative to high speeds is cooperative hunting. Lionesses often hunt together, one group driving the prey towards others concealed in the long grass. Wild hunting-dogs, hyaenas and wolves also hunt in packs, and can bring down prey much larger than themselves. Killer whales and some species of dolphin will cooperate to herd fish into shallow water, where they can easily be slaughtered. Groups of the larger pelican species can herd together large numbers of fish by swimming in horseshoe formation and gradually closing the circle to trap them. They often plunge their beaks simultaneously into the water to scoop up the fish.

Jill Bailey

Below: Plain- and prairie-dwellers like the Thompson's gazelle may seek safety in numbers as a means of defence against predatory birds such as the martial eagle. This is often insufficient protection and one graceful animal becomes a meal for another.

CAMOUFLAGE

When leaves suddenly get up and walk, when the sea bed grows tentacles and seizes an unwary fish, when a fly disappears into the 'jaws' of a pretty flower, camouflage has served its purpose. The purpose of camouflage is deceit, usually to conceal an animal from its predators, or to conceal a predator from its prey.

Some of the most effective disguises are seen in the fish and insects that match their surroundings in both colour and texture. Stonefish, scorpion fish and angler fish have tiny knobbly outgrowths from their skin that resemble the short growths of seaweed that coat the rocks among which they live. The leafy sea dragon's body is shaped like a piece of seaweed. It uses transparent fins to scull itself along, so that it waves and drifts in the water in the same way as the plant.

One of the great giveaways is shadow, which makes the animal appear dark below and pale above, so that it stands out against its surroundings. This can be disguised by countershading — colouring that produces the opposite effect, giving the animal a pale belly and dark back. Animals that perch on the trunks of trees or on rocks often have

Below: Bright colouring can often provide the best of disguises, particularly in spring. Small, tree-living creatures such as caterpillars may have no other defence than their ability to look like a leaf as they crawl slowly along a branch.

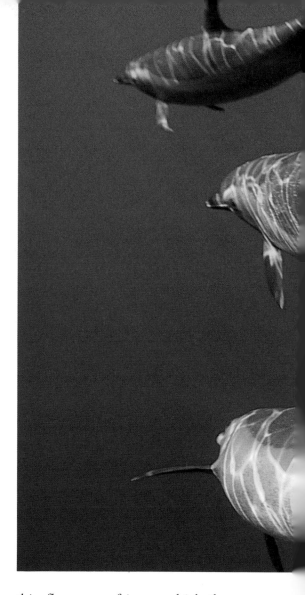

thin flanges or fringes which they press close to the surface to prevent any shadows from forming.

Shadow is not the only clue used by predators. Many are highly tuned to detect the shape or silhouette of their prey. Some of the boldest patterns in nature have evolved to overcome this problem. When a herd of giraffes takes to its heels, the confusion of blotches makes it difficult for a predator to pick out an individual animal.

Coral reef fish use stripes for camouflage, or have very bold patterns of brilliant colours that to our eyes appear highly conspicuous. But blocks of colour distract the eye from noticing the remainder of the animal's shape.

Many a juicy insect has evolved to look like a dry inedible object such as a dead leaf or twig. Stick insects are familiar examples, with their false knobbly nodes and worn-looking edges. There are also moths that resemble broken twigs, desert praying mantids that resemble round stones, and stick caterpillars that stick out rigidly at an angle to the main branch, just like a real twig. Leaf-mimic mantids often sway gently to and fro so that they appear to be blowing gently in the breeze. The leaf fish, when threatened, stops moving, and allows itself to drift gently to the bottom of the lake or river, looking like a dead leaf. It is remarkable how some quite bulky animals manage to resemble flat

Above: The countershading on dolphins protects them from would-be predators. When seen from above, the dark backs of these marine mammals blend with the surrounding water, and when looked at from below, their pale bellies merge with the light filtering through the water.

Left: The intricate patterning on the flattened back of the Colombian horned frog makes it look almost two-dimensional as it lies in wait for small rodents, lizards and other frogs. Its eyes are concealed from above by a hood and are dark, so as to blend with the debris and shadows on the forest floor.

Above: The bold stripes of a herd of zebra seem to blur in the middle distance and the outline of each individual becomes indistinct, confusing would-be predators, which find it difficult to single out one animal to attack from among the flying hooves and dust.

Right: The tiger's vertical stripes are a particularly effective camouflage in dense undergrowth or among the trees of the forest, where they blend in with the shadows and allow this massive cat to lie unnoticed as it waits for its victims.

objects like leaves. Leaf-mimic frogs of the tropics achieve this effect by having flattened backs, often with flanges that overhang their flanks. The pale colour of the back changes sharply to a dark shadow-like band at the edge of the flange. When viewed from above, the eyes are concealed by a ridge of flesh, and are dark to blend with the false shadow. Markings on legs and back match, so the frog's anatomy is difficult to distinguish.

Special postures and movements can enhance a good disguise. Macleay's spectre, a stick insect from Australia, mimics an ant when very young, running around in a jerky fashion. Older juveniles, too large for

emotions. Their colour change is under the rapid control of the nervous system, whereas that of the chameleon and most other animals is controlled by slower-acting chemicals (hormones).

Not all animals rely on their own disguises. Some borrow them. Decorator crabs and some kinds of bug have bodies covered in bristles upon which they impale pieces of weed and debris that they pick up from their surroundings. Caddis larvae construct intricate cases from pieces of weed, tiny snail shells, stones and dead twigs. Cuttlefish, flatfish and rays, which often lie in wait on the sea bed for their prey, flick sand over their backs until only their eyes are visible.

This world of deceit and counter-deceit presents a challenge to the naturalist and nature watcher. Many a landscape that appears barren, and many a tree or bush that looks devoid of life, in fact supports a miniature population of its own, visible only to the experienced eye. Yet without the need for camouflage and deceit, some of nature's most bizarre and beautiful creatures would never have evolved.

Jill Bailey

Above: Birds active at night may use camouflaged plumage to hide them during the day. The potoo is streaked and mottled to resemble a branch. When danger approaches, its ability to freeze, with its head pointing skywards, enhances this disguise.

Below: The flat shape and cryptic colouring of a flatfish allows it to blend perfectly with its surroundings as it lies motionless on the sea bed.

such pretences, stretch out their forelegs and raise their tails like scorpions if frightened. The adults resemble clusters of curled-up dead leaves.

A few animals are able to change colour in response to a changing background. Some, like flatfish and bottom-dwelling rays, take a considerable time to change, but can achieve a good match eventually. The chameleon is somewhat quicker, while squid and cuttlefish can show a kaleidoscope of colours in just a few seconds. These remarkable molluscs use a range of colours and patterns to blend with different backgrounds and to communicate with each other and express

WILDLIFE IN DANGER

It is one of the more sobering facts of life that the fate of all individual living organisms is to die. It is similarly true that every one of the planet's multitude of life forms is also ultimately doomed to disappear. In fact, since life first began 3.5 billion years ago, 90 per cent of all the species of animal and plant that ever existed have completely died out. This process of extinction is quite normal, and can also be very gradual — for example, a species like the coelacanth, a deep-sea fish from the Indian Ocean, appeared on the planet 300–700 million years ago, yet survives to this day.

However, in the last 400 years the rate at which animals and plants have disappeared has accelerated unnaturally, because of the effect of the earth's single most successful species — *Homo sapiens*. Human beings have colonized every portion of the globe, their population swelling to over 5 billion in the 1990s. This remarkable expansion now exerts a profoundly destructive effect on the rest of life. It is estimated that, of all the earth's millions of species, as many as a million could become extinct by the end of

the century. Within a further few decades, several more million species could also have vanished. This extinction rate could mean more than four species disappearing every single hour — a situation described by one eminent ecologist as 'a biological débâcle greater than all mass extinctions of the past put together'.

There are four principal causes of this vast number of extinctions: loss of habitat, over-exploitation, the introduction of alien species (such as the spread of rats on to remote islands) and the impact of pollution. By far the most critical of these factors is loss of habitat. All the major ecosystems, including forest, grassland and wetland, have dwindled because of the ever-increasing demands imposed by humans. In the last thousand years almost two-thirds of the planet's forests, which once covered half of all the land surface, have been felled to make way for agriculture and to provide fuel and timber.

One tropical region that has experienced forest destruction on a massive scale is Madagascar in the Indian Ocean, to the south-east of Africa. The world's fourth largest island, Madagascar has been isolated from the African continent for 100 million years, and now possesses many species of animal and plant that occur nowhere else. The island is thought to have 15 or so species of lemur, ranging in size from the tiny ground mouse lemur, which weighs only 60g, to species weighing as much as 10kg. These distant relations of monkeys and apes, with their long arms and legs, usually long tails, soft woolly fur, fox-like faces and large inexpressive eyes, are almost all vegetarian tree-dwellers. During their long isolation they have developed a wide range of specialist lifestyles, which have made them vulnerable to the changes wrought by

Above: Loss of habitat is a major factor in the extinction of species. In recent years the tropical rainforests, thought to shelter as many as 2–5 million species have been cleared at a rate of 76,000–100,000sq km per year — an area roughly equivalent to the size of Austria.

may number no more than 50, making it one of the world's rarest mammals.

While the loss of forest threatens the greatest diversity of life, other habitats, such as grassland, have also been severely depleted. In Africa, Australia and parts of Asia and North America, open savannah, steppe and prairie lands have been converted into farmland and their natural grazing communities displaced by domestic livestock. Many mammals have declined dramatically as a result — for example, Przewalski's horse, the Asiatic and African wild asses, the Bactrian camel, the giraffe and the pronghorn of North America. In North America alone, the original prairie that once extended over 1 million sq km has been reduced to only 16,000sq km. Much of this habitat destruction took place during the great westward expansion of European colonists, whose classic victim was the continent's largest land mammal, the American bison.

There were once as many as 50-60 million of these huge herbivores, but from the 1850s onwards their numbers fell catastrophically because of measures pursued by white settlers. Vast tracts of grassland were rapidly enclosed and converted for agricultural use, while the construction of railways disrupted bison migration routes and divided the herds into isolated populations. Squeezed into ever more restricted areas, the bison were also subjected to large-scale slaughter to provide meat, hide and other products. A third factor was a policy of deliberate systematic extermination, as part of a wider strategy to defeat the Plains Indians like the Sioux, with whom the European colonists were at war. Within a 15-year period, from 1870 to 1885, the bison was all but eliminated.

Only as extinction loomed did a few enlightened conservationists struggle to ensure the legal protection of the remaining 1000 individuals. These were held in reserves such as the Yellowstone National Park in

humans. Since the arrival of the first colonists about AD500, 14 species of lemur have been exterminated. With the clearance of 80 per cent of the natural vegetation, especially Madagascar's rich coastal forest, all the existing species are now considered to be at risk.

One of the most critically threatened is the aye-aye, an extraordinary cat-sized primate with huge bat-like ears, a rodent's front teeth and extremely long bony third fingers. This nocturnal mammal listens intently for the wood-boring insect larvae on which it feeds, and then gnaws at the dead wood, finally extracting its prey with its probe-like fingers. This century the aye-aye has been a tragic casualty of habitat loss and persecution by the superstitious Malagasy people, who believe the animal to be a harbinger of evil. For years the aye-aye was thought to be extinct until a small number was rediscovered in 1957. Nine individuals were captured and re-released on the Nosy Mangabé island reserve off the mainland, where they have now bred. But the aye-aye's tiny and fragile population

Wyoming, USA, and the Wood Buffalo National Park in Alberta, Canada. This century, bison numbers have steadily increased to about 50,000, with two-thirds of these in the United States. However, the clearance of the continent's grasslands means that the species will probably never reach even 1 per cent of its former numbers.

Habitat loss need not be focused on one particular region for it to have a very severe impact. The Siberian crane is a species now threatened with extinction, partly because of wetland reclamation that has gone on for many decades over immense areas. It formerly bred across a broad 3000km belt of Soviet Siberian tundra and then wintered in an equally extensive range from the Caspian Sea to eastern China. Piecemeal drainage of wetlands in these two areas, as well as along the bird's 5000km migration route, has helped reduce the population of this magnificent white bird to about 2000. Worldwide these same processes now threaten a further 25 species of large wading bird such as the white-bellied heron and the greater adjutant stork, 20 species of wildfowl and six other species of crane.

The Siberian crane is one of the most critically endangered because of its vulnerability to disturbance and its massive habitat requirements. A thousand square kilometres of tundra within the breeding range may hold only one or two pairs, and these

Below: The sifaka of Madagascar belongs to the rare family of leaping lemurs. Its body is uniquely adapted to leaping between the tree trunks, so that when it is on the ground it moves with an extraordinary hopping motion. The sifaka is severely endangered by habitat loss, and cannot be maintained in zoos as it does not thrive in captivity.

Right: The American bison is the continent's largest land mammal, weighing up to 1 tonne, and its population once represented perhaps the largest concentration of mammals the world has ever known. The bison is a spectacular example of how a species of vast numbers can quickly be brought to the verge of extinction by human actions.

will nest at least 25km apart. During migration and in its winter quarters the species faces additional pressures. At Poyang Lake in east central China, where more than 90 per cent of the world population of these cranes has been known to winter, excessive drainage and low rainfall have forced the birds into areas where they are at risk from hunting and poison. At the only known wintering site in India, Bharatpur Bird Sanctuary, the population has dwindled to 17, due to the loss of wetland habitat within the reserve and to hunting in Afghanistan and Pakistan during the crane's migration.

A recent joint Soviet-American initiative to boost numbers has involved establishing a captive breeding programme and placing Siberian crane eggs under nesting common cranes, which winter in large numbers at relatively safe sites in Iran. It is hoped that the foster parents will raise the chicks and then teach them their own migration route, thus establishing a new and more secure population of Siberian cranes wintering in Iran.

The second major cause of extinction — direct human exploitation for food and other resources — has been in operation since almost the first appearance of mankind.

Early stone-age hunters helped exterminate many large prehistoric mammals like the woolly mammoth and woolly rhinoceros. It was exactly this factor that led to the demise of some of the best-known extinct species: the dodo (1662), the great auk (1844) and the passenger pigeon (1914). However, one of the animals that was most rapidly eliminated was Steller's sea cow. At 6–9m long this was the largest mammal outside the whale group. It was an entirely aquatic vegetarian and inhabited the Bering Sea, off Bering Island and the Komandorskiye Islands. Russian hunters caught these docile animals to provision their ships with meat and hide, often fatally wounding many more than they could catch. By 1768, only 27 years after the sea cow was first discovered, it had become extinct.

As well as being highly successful and often merciless hunters, humans have carried with them during their colonization of the globe a whole camp-following of other animals such as domestic stock, monkeys, dogs, cats, mongooses and rats. Frequently these species have been introduced to remote archipelagos, where unique island

Below: The Siberian crane is one of several species of crane now on the verge of extinction, due mainly to the continued erosion of its natural habitat. This is not helped by the fact that each pair requires a vast territory of its own in which to breed.

Today a further 15 of New Zealand's birds are threatened with extinction, partly because of the impact of alien predators. One of the most critically endangered is the kakapo. This, the world's heaviest parrot, is both flightless and nocturnal and was once found throughout much of North, South and Stewart Islands. However, the clearance of three-quarters of New Zealand's forests and the depredations of introduced stoats have been key factors in the kakapo's massive decline. In 1990 there were only 43 individuals left. Almost all of these survivors have been transferred to small offshore islands, like Little Barrier Island, that are free of terrestrial mammals. It is hoped that, in their new protected environments and with the benefits of supplementary foods, these relict populations can finally be encouraged to breed and multiply.

The fourth factor in the current phase of extinctions is the lethal cocktail of chemicals with which industrial societies have

communities of plants and animals have developed in the absence of terrestrial mammals. The impact of the invading predators has invariably been devastating. Island birds, many of which have lost the power of flight, have been especially affected by these introductions — 90 per cent of all the birds that have become extinct since 1600 have been from islands.

One of the bird communities that has been most seriously disrupted is that of New Zealand. Even before the arrival of Europeans, the early Polynesian colonists and their entourage of dogs and rats had caused the extinction of several giant bird species known as moas. From the eighteenth century onwards, British settlers introduced a much larger number of predators such as stoats and weasels into a land whose only mammals had previously been bats. Within 200 years at least another six birds were extinct, including the Stephen Island wren. This unfortunate species, endemic to one tiny islet, was exterminated in the same year that it was described and by the very animal that first discovered it — a lighthouse-keeper's cat!

Below: Tiger populations have been alarmingly reduced by a combination of habitat destruction and intensive hunting. In 1972 the World Wildlife Fund (later the World Wide Fund for Nature) launched Operation Tiger, which led to international legal protection, a trade ban on all tiger products and the creation of over 40 reserves throughout the tiger's range.

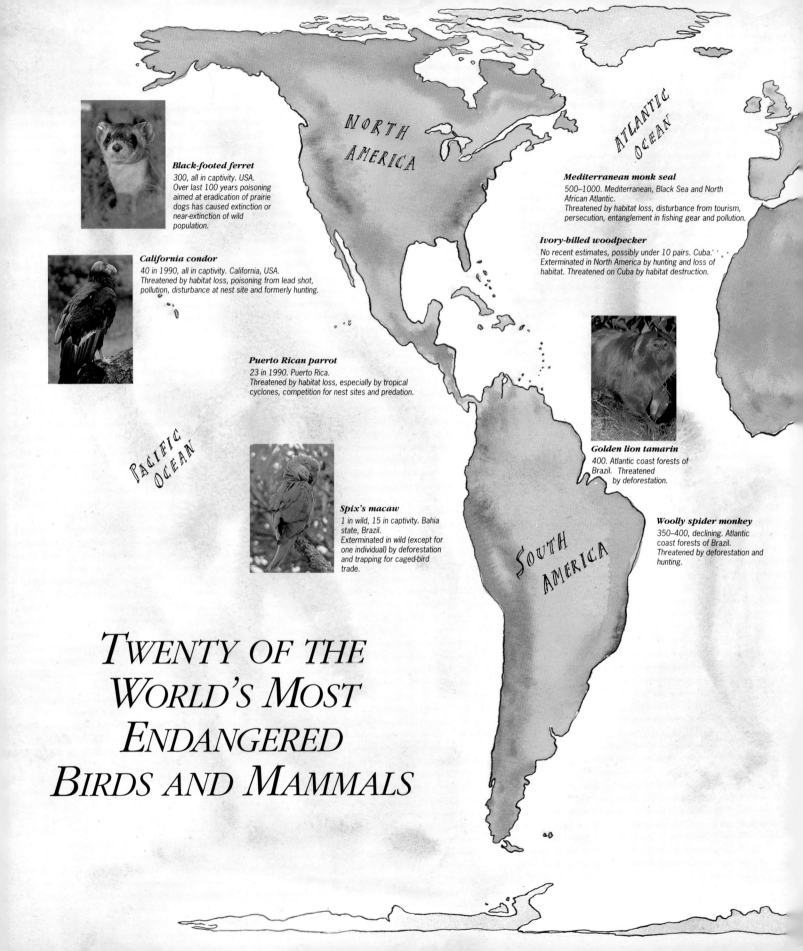

Black-footed ferret
300, all in captivity. USA.
Over last 100 years poisoning
aimed at eradication of prairie
dogs has caused extinction or
near-extinction of wild
population.

Mediterranean monk seal
500–1000. Mediterranean, Black Sea and North
African Atlantic.
Threatened by habitat loss, disturbance from tourism,
persecution, entanglement in fishing gear and pollution.

Ivory-billed woodpecker
No recent estimates, possibly under 10 pairs. Cuba.
Exterminated in North America by hunting and loss of
habitat. Threatened on Cuba by habitat destruction.

California condor
40 in 1990, all in captivity. California, USA.
Threatened by habitat loss, poisoning from lead shot,
pollution, disturbance at nest site and formerly hunting.

Puerto Rican parrot
23 in 1990. Puerto Rica.
Threatened by habitat loss, especially by tropical
cyclones, competition for nest sites and predation.

Golden lion tamarin
400. Atlantic coast forests of
Brazil. Threatened
by deforestation.

Spix's macaw
1 in wild, 15 in captivity. Bahia
state, Brazil.
Exterminated in wild (except for
one individual) by deforestation
and trapping for caged-bird
trade.

Woolly spider monkey
350–400, declining. Atlantic
coast forests of Brazil.
Threatened by deforestation and
hunting.

NORTH AMERICA

SOUTH AMERICA

ATLANTIC OCEAN

PACIFIC OCEAN

TWENTY OF THE WORLD'S MOST ENDANGERED BIRDS AND MAMMALS

EUROPE

ASIA

AFRICA

PACIFIC OCEAN

Javan rhinoceros
60–69. Java and Vietnam.
Threatened by loss of lowland
rainforest and poaching for
traditional oriental medicine.

Baiji or Yangtze River dolphin
300, decline believed to be continuing. Yangtze River,
China.
Threatened by entanglement in fishing gear, collisions
with boats and wetland reclamation.

Crested ibis
Approximately 40. Shaanxi Province, China.
Declined because of human persecution, especially
hunting. Threatened by habitat loss.

Gurney's pitta
30. Southern Thailand.
Threatened by deforestation and trapping for the
caged-bird trade.

Iriomote cat
40–80. Japanese-owned Iriomote Island off Taiwan.
Threatened by habitat destruction, disturbance from
tourism, opposition of islanders to conservation
measures.

Pygmy hog
100–150 (1978 census).
Assam, India.
Threatened by destruction of
grasslands and hunting.

Philippine eagle
150–200. Islands of Leyte,
Luzon, Mindanao and Samar in
Philippines.
Threatened by deforestation.

Kouprey
100–300. Vietnam, Laos, Cambodia and Thailand.
Threatened by uncontrolled hunting, habitat loss.

INDIAN OCEAN

Tamaraw
356 (1987 census). Island of Mindoro, Philippines.
Threatened by hunting and deforestation.

Seychelles magpie-robin
24 in 1990. Fregate Island, Seychelles.
Threatened by habitat loss and predation by introduced
species.

AUSTRALASIA

Mauritius parakeet
10. Mauritius.
Threatened by habitat loss,
competition and predation by
introduced species.

OCEANIA

Kakapo
43 in 1990. Offshore islands in
New Zealand.
Threatened by predation from
introduced mammals.

ANTARCTICA

polluted the earth, seas and air. Though pollution is seldom exclusively responsible for exterminating an entire species, it has played a critical role in the decline of many animals, especially birds. Some of the most destructive chemicals are the organochlorine pesticides, like DDT, dieldrin and aldrin, which have been used almost worldwide since the 1940s. These toxic compounds pass through the food chain and eventually build up in the bodies of flesh-eating birds, like birds of prey. High doses can result in death, but even at sub-lethal levels they cause infertility or the production of eggs with unnaturally thin shells, which the parent birds then accidentally break in the nest.

One of the most spectacular and endangered species to have suffered from this form of pollution is the California condor. Its numbers decreased enormously after the arrival of Europeans in North America and this century it has been largely confined to the south-west coast of the United States. During its final years in the wild, the condor's breeding success had been abysmally poor: in the 1960s and 1970s the entire population of about 50 birds was producing only two fledged young a year. This failure was partly because of pesticide contamination. Another serious cause of the condor's decline has been poisoning from lead shot that the birds ingested from the carcases of animals on which they fed. With condor numbers ever dwindling, it was decided in 1987 to take the entire population of 27 into 'protective custody' and initiate a complex captive breeding and re-release programme, which now represents the bird's last chance for survival.

Some biologists have argued that ultimately this is bound to fail, and that the California condor, like the other 90 per cent of species that have ever existed on earth, is doomed to extinction through natural processes. They point to the fact that, in the prehistoric past, the condor underwent a massive decline as the large prehistoric mammals on which the bird once fed also became extinct.

However, there is little doubt that the population collapse in the last 200 years has been a direct result of human persecution and human changes to the environment. Should it disappear completely, then the California condor — like the other four species that are believed to face extinction every hour — will be silent testimony to our seemingly unlimited capacity for destruction and our failure to act in time.

Mark Cocker

Below: The rare and elusive aye-aye is the only living member of its family. Only a handful now survive in a small pocket of the Madagascan rainforest, making it one of the rarest and most endangered of all mammals.

BRITAIN'S ENDANGERED SPECIES

Britain is among the most densely populated regions on earth and has been settled by humans since prehistoric times. Humans have also imposed dramatic changes on the landscape, which have often had a damaging impact on the British flora and fauna.

Within recorded history, many species prized for their meat and pelts, and large carnivores that competed with humans, have completely disappeared. Brown bears were probably eliminated before the tenth century AD, and beavers survived for only a further 300 years, victims of lowland deforestation and over-exploitation. Wild boar, too, vanished by the seventeenth century, although the wolf hung on in northernmost Scotland, retreating in the face of continuous persecution, until hunted out in about 1740.

The reduction in wetlands, particularly the Fens, wiped out common cranes in the reign of Elizabeth I, while conversion of open grasslands and hunting ensured that East Anglia's last great bustards had gone by 1832. In the late nineteenth century and throughout this century loss of habitat has accelerated. Half of Britain's hedgerows and woodlands, 90 per cent of heathland and all but 3 per cent of traditional meadowlands have gone. As these habitats have dwindled, so have their populations of animals. Heathland species, for instance, like the sand lizard, smooth snake, nightjar and stone curlew, are all now endangered in Britain.

Pollution has presented another major threat to British wildlife. The greater horseshoe bat, like all Britain's 14 other species of bat, has declined catastrophically, partly because of the widespread use of pesticides. It is estimated that the current population of under 1000 represents just 1 per cent of its original numbers. The decline of British otters has also coincided with the widespread pollution of waters by pesticides and industrial chemicals.

Since mammals like the otter and greater horseshoe bat have extensive ranges on the continent of Europe, their disappearance from Britain would not signal the end of the species. However, very often the factors that threaten a population in Britain have the same impact elsewhere. Animals like the stone curlew, otter and greater horseshoe bat are declining not just in Britain but throughout Europe. One of the best ways to safeguard a species on an international level, then, is to arrest any local decline and maintain the greatest regional diversity of flora and fauna.

Above: The sand lizard is arguably Britain's rarest reptile, although it is rather more common in the rest of Europe.

TEN OF BRITAIN'S MOST THREATENED SPECIES

1 *European otter* (Lutra lutra)
2 *Bechstein's bat* (Myotis bechsteini)
3 *Greater horseshoe bat* (Rhinolophus ferrumequinum)
4 *Sand lizard* (Lacerta agilis)
5 *Smooth snake* (Coronella austriaca)
6 *Red kite* (Milvus milvus)
7 *Corncrake* (Crex crex)
8 *Roseate tern* (Sterna dougallii)
9 *Bittern* (Botaurus stellaris)
10 *Montagu's harrier* (Circus pygargus)

Left: The red kite is now one of the rarest breeding birds in Britain. This magnificent predator with its glowing red plumage lives in the hillside woods of central Wales.

Environmental Issues

Our environment is changing, faster now than ever before. In the name of progress, we are bringing about radical transformations. This section explores some of our most beautiful wilderness areas and the threats to them, discovering how easily the delicate ecological balance can be upset.

Wetlands which contain an enormous variety of wildlife are under threat, while coral reefs, fabulous underwater gardens full of colour and life, are being destroyed. The Antarctic has survived as the one last great wilderness, untouched and unspoilt by human expansion — but for how much longer? Closer to home, Europe's remaining wildlife is being eroded, although conservation schemes are helping.

The Gulf War was the latest, chilling example of the devastatingly harmful effect mankind can have on the natural world. Finishing with an examination of the wildlife trade today, this part of the book takes a realistic look at the continuing threats to wildlife habitats and what is being done to solve them.

Above: Botswana is a southern African country dominated by the vast Kalahari Desert. But towards its northern borde lies the lush and fertile area of the mighty Okavango Delta.

Above Left: Volcanoes are among the most destructive natural forces on earth, having claimed the lives of a quarter of a million people over the last 600 years. This is Oldoinyo, an active volcano in Tanzania.

Left: Antarctica is the last great wilderness on earth. It is a vast and lonely continent, covering an area of 14,108,000sq km. With a lowest recorded temperature of −89.2°C, it is also the coldest place on the planet.

WETLANDS

Wetland habitats are found in all parts of the world. They are areas of waterlogged land that vary in size from small boggy patches to huge swamps, such as the Everglades in Florida or the Camargue in France. Wetlands may be freshwater, formed when streams or rivers reach flat land and spread into a sprawl of interconnecting pools and canals, or they may be salty, coastal marshes, such as the mangrove swamps of south-east Asia and Australia or the coastal mudflats and reed swamps of Europe.

The animals and plants that live in these unique habitats vary with the way in which the wetlands are formed, whether they are seasonal or permanent, and the local climate. Some of the world's greatest wildlife spectacles are to be seen in wetlands. Many species, especially birds, exist in these regions and nowhere else, and depend on wetlands for their survival. There are huge flocks of migrating and overwintering waterfowl and waders that gather to rest, feed and breed on temperate and northern lakes and reservoirs; hippos, crocodiles and abundant fish populations that support large numbers of human settlements live in tropical swamps; and water birds and waders are found in coastal saltmarshes and mangrove swamps, which also provide nurseries for countless fish and crustaceans. Wetlands are prized, too, for their scenic beauty — the ever-changing patterns of water, plants, clouds and wildlife with colours that vary with time and weather.

Some of the most important wetlands for birdlife are found on the coast. The shallow waters of coastal swamps, enriched by organic material from their plants and animals, form important feeding grounds for fish, crustaceans and other marine life, which in turn attract a remarkable range of birds. Huge numbers of birds migrate over these

Right: The Okavango is one of a series of great lakes and wetlands scattered along the African Rift Valley. Game animals of the African plains gather there to drink, and inhabitants include crocodiles, swamp antelopes, rare slaty egrets, African fish eagles, Pel's fishing owls, reed cormorants and kingfishers.

Above: The flamingo is perhaps the best-known inhabitant of the Camargue. The bird's long legs allow it to wade through deep water in search of food.

Wetlands have always attracted humans — their beauty, the lushness of the vegetation and the teeming wildlife attract tourists, naturalists, and hunters. In the United States in particular, many wetlands owe their continued existence to hunters, who have a vested interest in the well-being of wetlands and their wildlife. In warm countries, wetlands provide essential watering places for cattle and other livestock, and irrigation water for agriculture. However, many of the world's greatest wetlands are now under serious threat from human activity. Irrigation of nearby farmland can draw water away from wetlands, and in coastal regions this may allow salt water to percolate into the wetlands from the sea, sometimes contaminating underground water sources. Coastal wetlands and deltas are drying out as irrigation upstream deprives the rivers of water, and dams also reduce the sediment load, decreasing the fertility of the coastal plains.

areas, and they also provide important over-wintering areas for birds that breed on the northern tundra in summer. Deltas the world over attract birdlife, and the lush swamp vegetation that fringes them is often home, too, to a range of mammals and reptiles. For example, the Sundarbans of the Bay of Bengal supports tigers, deer and crocodiles, as well as pheasants and a host of other birds. Alligators, deer and the rare Florida panther live in the Everglades, and pelicans, ibises, storks, herons and egrets nest there.

The disruption of seasonal flooding regimes by flood control programmes and reservoirs can also have serious consequences for the wetland wildlife. Dams and barrages block the migration of fish such as salmon and eels, while the reinforcement of river banks prevents many riverine fish from spreading into the inundated floodplains to breed. In Egypt, the vast amounts of sediment trapped by the Aswan dam, which originally made possible the creation of a large new area of farmland, now prevent the Nile delta from maintaining itself against the encroachment of the sea.

In addition to providing an important habitat for plants, birds and other animals, wetlands serve other essential functions. They act rather like sponges that soak up storm waters and release them gradually into the rivers, helping to prevent damage. In river floodplains water spreads out across the land, dropping its silt to create fertile soils. Reeds and other wetland plants are able to trap many water pollutants, thus improving the quality of water downstream. As the water slows in the wetlands, it sinks into the ground to recharge underground water stores which may supply water to human populations over a very large area. Coastal wetlands form vital barriers against erosion by the sea, dissipating the energy of the waves.

Some of the most vital wetlands are the great swamps of the continental interiors, such as the Okavango and Etosha in southern Africa, where rivers cannot survive to reach the sea, but end in a vast swamp that periodically dries out to form extensive salt pans. The Okavango's great diversity of wildlife is due to the juxtaposition of wetlands and arid land, of permanent residents and temporary visitors.

Left: The Camargue, one of the three most important wetland sites in Europe, provides the shallow, very salty lakes that the flamingo needs. Each year, flocks of as many as 10,000 individuals visit the region to breed.

Above: The Spanish imperial eagle is one of the birds threatened by development schemes at the Coto Doñana National Park. Less than a hundred pairs of this species survive today. There is considerable pressure on its habitat, but it is vital to preserve the areas of open land needed by the eagle to hunt its prey.

Originally sparsely populated, the Okavango was protected from herdsmen by the prevalence of the tsetse fly, a carrier of the disease sleeping sickness that affects both humans and their livestock (native mammals are immune). Recent attempts to eradicate the pest have been successful, and there are now fears that herdsmen and their cattle will encroach on the delta, overgrazing the vegetation and depriving wildlife of its main food base. A new government-sponsored project is attempting to encourage wildlife ranching — the rearing of native mammals for meat to feed the people of Botswana.

The Botswana government is also trying to encourage local people to improve the quality of their cattle, rather than allowing an increase in cattle numbers, by encouraging the sale of beef for export. However,

subsidies from the European Community (EC), the main importer of Botswana beef, result in artificially high prices, which again tempt the herdsmen to try to keep too many cattle. The EC also requires the cattle to be free of foot-and-mouth disease. Vaccination is not sufficient protection, since the native water buffalo and warthogs carry the disease, so fences now separate the cattle from the buffalo. This caused thousands of deaths by preventing grazing mammals from following their normal migration routes. But it has granted the delta a reprieve from the cattle and the whole delta has now been declared a cattle-free area.

The eradication of the tsetse fly has permitted the development of a burgeoning tourism and hunting industry in Botswana, fortunately carefully controlled by the government to prevent too much damage to the ecosystem. Hunting is providing new jobs and income for the local people, and foreign hunters pay high prices to shoot wildlife. Licences from the government control the numbers and species of wildlife that can be hunted. Cheaper licences enable the local people to hunt animals for food, but this system is prone to abuse, since the skins of the animals, when cured, sell for high prices overseas. The Botswana government is environment-conscious, and a comprehensive land use plan is being drawn up to establish specific areas for protection, tribal settlement, wildlife management, hunting and tourism.

Probably the main threat to the Okavango is from increased water demand. The nearby frontier town of Maun is one of the fastest-growing in the country, with over 30,000 inhabitants. A diamond mine at Orapa will require increasingly large amounts of water to be extracted by damming and dredging rivers that feed the swamp. Both Orapa and Maun want to tap the Okavango River to the north, which has water to spare, but this would be an expensive and difficult engineering project. Much cheaper is a plan to channel the water of the southern delta between banks, but this would dry out vital parts of the swamp. At present, boreholes are being dug to tap ancient underground water, but this supply is limited, and if exhausted may also result in desertification. International help has been forthcoming — the EC is funding a Wildlife Training Centre to provide scouts to enforce conservation laws, and it is hoped that a loan from the World Bank will help to solve overgrazing and livestock management problems.

Tourism is a serious problem for many wetlands in Europe and North America. Coto Doñana in Spain, one of the last strongholds of the Spanish lynx and Spanish imperial eagle, is threatened by tourism and drainage schemes. Until recently it had remained relatively unspoilt, protected as a royal hunting reserve. But beautiful coastal areas attract tourists, and Spain's Atlantic coast is one of the major tourist destinations in Europe. For the last two years, the park has been threatened by plans for a new luxury resort, Costa Doñana, on the margin of the Doñana Park, which would necessitate the destruction of part of the dune system. The development would extend along some 6km of pristine beach close to the existing resort of Matalascañas, and would house up to an extra 32,000 holiday-makers, with a golf course, parks, gardens and a polo pitch all needing to be watered. There are fears that the extraction of water for the development could upset the hydrological balance of the Doñana marshes by drawing fresh water away from the lagoons and allowing salt water to enter in its place. Waste and rubbish could also pollute the waters, and the noise and disturbance may upset the large numbers of breeding birds.

France's Camargue, on the Rhône delta, is a rather special place famous for its flamingos and wild horses. It contains a mixture of fresh

Below: An extensive complex of dunes, heaths, woodlands and wetlands at the mouth of the River Guadiana, Coto Doñana National Park is home to large populations of waterfowl, and an important migration staging post for many more. It is also rich in small mammals and reptiles. This century, 60 per cent of Spain's wetlands have disappeared.

and salt water. The Camargue is a huge wetland covering some 1450sq km, a complex mosaic of fresh, brackish and salt water marshes and ponds; beaches and dunes; reed beds, pastureland and dykes; grasslands and woods. On a major migration route between Africa and Europe, it forms a vital winter refuge and migration staging post for millions of ducks, geese and waders, and supports a large breeding population of birds. It is one of only three or four breeding sites in Europe for the greater flamingo, which is encouraged by the provision of artificial nest mounds. The reed beds provide nesting sites for bitterns, herons and other marshland birds.

The delicate hydrological balance of the Camargue is being disturbed by the expansion of rice paddies on adjacent land and by the proposed development of tourist villages at the coast, bringing an inevitable rise in demand for water. Much of the Camargue lies within protected areas, but outside these areas salt extraction beds and industrial sites cover over 50 per cent of the land, a dramatic increase in the last 40 years. Since the Second World War, many rice paddies have been established. These upset the drainage of the area, and the

balance between fresh and salt water. There is also tourist pressure, since many pilgrims visit Santes-Maries-de-la-Mer, and ornithologists also frequent the Camargue.

The world's wetlands are to some extent regulated by a series of international agreements and initiatives. In 1991 representatives from 28 countries met in Grado, Italy, to develop a strategy for protecting Mediterranean wetlands. The outcome was a plan to identify the exact extent of the wetland areas and their problems, to regulate population growth and tourism in the areas, and to investigate irrigation schemes, coupled with attempts to evolve more re-use of water. The symposium decided that water resources in the Mediterranean should be managed on a catchment basis (according to the area from which water is drawn by particular river systems, rather than on a political country-by-country basis). Water use in one country can have serious effects on water availability in countries downstream. It is hoped that the Mediterranean countries will attempt to predict the demand for water for all purposes — drinking, irrigation (including the problems of salt accumulation in irrigated land and drainage waters), dilution of waste, water transport, recreation, fisheries, control of underground water supplies, and flow of sediments and nutrients to coastal regions. Then plans can be made to conserve wetland resources, supported by joint sharing of information and research.

On a world scale is the Convention on Wetlands of International Importance set up at Ramsar in Italy in 1971. Signatories to the Convention, which covers artificial as well as natural wetlands, agree to list their important wetlands and maintain them as they are, and to plan sustainable use of these areas, including the setting-up of nature reserves. Within Europe, there are about 300 sites declared as protected wetlands under the Ramsar Convention. Despite the agreement, many Ramsar-designated wetlands are under serious threat from human activities. In coastal areas, some marshes and mudflats — both vital as feeding, breeding and roosting areas for birds — may be unable to keep up with the rising sea level, resulting in inundation. Moreover, coastal defences and human activities such as agriculture may block the retreat of these wetlands inland.

The Bonn Convention on Migratory Species of 1979 attempted to protect the migration routes of birds, but so far not enough countries have signed the Convention to provide protection for whole routes, particularly in Africa, Asia and South America. Coastal areas are also covered by the United Nations Environment Programme's Regional Seas Programme, which supports programmes to clean up pollution and protect marine habitats.

Throughout the world there is increasing recognition of the importance of wetland wilderness areas. Nevertheless, the rapid growth of the world population means that ever-increasing demands for water are likely to generate conflict, especially in regions of limited water supply. Wetlands are not only important wildlife resources — they are vital to the survival of human life.

Jill Bailey

Below: The hippopotamus is a permanent resident of the Okavango. A wetland environment is essential to the animal's welfare, since its unique skin structure causes it to lose moisture at a rapid rate in the air. The threat to the waters of the Okavango could be the end of the hippopotamus's existence there.

SEA GARDENS

Coral reefs are unique in being the only substantial and lasting structures on earth (apart from man-made ones) that are built by living organisms. They are among the most complex ecosystems known to science, inhabited by a wide range of organisms whose evolutionary history goes back millions of years. Coral reefs teem with life, even though many are found in the open ocean where the surrounding water is relatively barren. This is achieved mainly through a highly effective system evolved by reefs for trapping and recycling essential nutrients.

Their structural complexity, together with the vast diversity of life-forms that the reefs support, makes them extremely important. They are also beautiful, provide man with food and other natural products, and protect land by acting as natural breakwaters.

Reef-building corals belong to a primitive animal phylum (main division of the animal kingdom) called the Coelenterata. Most are anemone-like, but a few are more closely related to sea firs and soft corals. Despite these differences, all so-called 'hard' corals secrete limestone around their bodies (polyps), to form a solid external skeleton. Reef-building corals live in colonies, the form of which depends on the species of coral and where on the reef it is growing. Some colonies are branched, bushy, or tree-like; others form plates or flat tables, encrustations, rounded heads, scrolls or pillars.

Corals grow at a rate of only a few centimetres a year, but their skeletons remain to form the basic structure of the reef. Probably the most widespread man-made cause of damage to living corals is the recent increase in levels of sediment in coastal waters. Coral polyps can remove only a certain amount from their bodies; beyond that they are smothered and die. The reef framework itself

Right: For corals to survive, particular conditions of water clarity, depth and temperature must all be right. These tend to be most readily met in the shallow waters surrounding islands in the Pacific and Indian Oceans.

Above: A healthy coral reef teems with fish of all kinds, shapes and sizes. It is thought that Australia's Great Barrier Reef contains about a tenth of all the world's known species of fish.

where levels of nutrients are high, but their smaller relations, microscopic single-celled algae, are of enormous importance. Millions are packed into the tissues of reef-building corals and pass to them products of their photosynthesis. It is this association between plants and animals that enables corals in the tropics to grow so fast that they form reefs. Many other reef organisms, including the giant clam, engage in a similar relationship. Benefits are mutual. The algae thrive in a safe, nutrient-rich, well-lit environment, while the animal has its waste products removed and converted into organic material, some of which is passed back from the algae to its host.

Tiny crabs live in their thousands among coral branches and larger ones hide in holes and caverns. Along with molluscs such as sea-snails, they usually come out and hunt during the night. Many of the shells are rare, yet they are avidly sought after by tourists and traders. Even starfish are collected and dried, while sea-urchin spines are used to make trinkets and jewellery.

Healthy reefs teem with fish of all kinds and of all shapes and sizes. Probably the most common small ones are damselfish. Some are solitary and tend gardens of algae; others hover around the coral in small

is also damaged in a number of ways. Hurricanes can have a devastating effect, but again, human activities such as mining for limestone and the removal of coral for the souvenir trade are responsible for reef degradation in many parts of the world.

Soft corals, sea-whips, sea-fans, sea-squirts, giant anemones, sponges of curious shapes and textures and many other colourful and exotic creatures are attached to the reef surface. Large seaweeds are less obvious, except

Right: Soft corals may grow to cover the sea floor in warm and shallow waters. They form fleshy, lobed or tree-like colonies which lack the limestone secretions of the hard, reef-building corals.

aggregations, or form plankton-feeding shoals above the reef surface. Wrasse, too, are plentiful and so are parrot-fish, which feed on coral using their strong beak-like teeth, leaving behind characteristic white scars. Some butterfly-fish also feed on coral, but in a much more delicate way, by picking at individual polyps using their long snouts.

In open water just off the reef face are shoals of fusiliers, snappers, surgeon-fish and jacks. More formidable are the lean and hungry predators such as barracuda, and hammerhead and white-tip sharks.

Edible reef fish are caught with rod and line, spears, nets and traps. Fishing intensity has reached high levels and over-exploitation is a growing concern. The use of traps often results in broken corals, but even worse is 'fishing' with explosives. Despite being illegal, this practice continues in some countries and causes widespread and indiscriminate damage to the reef habitat and its occupants. On top of this, many exotic reef fish are caught live for the aquarium trade.

Coral reefs are coming under increasing stress, and they and their resources need careful management. While the establishment of marine parks is not an answer to every problem, it helps to focus attention on particularly important reefs and allows the introduction of relevant conservation measures. The first marine park to include coral reefs was the John Pennekamp Coral Reef State Park, established in Florida in 1961. There are now around 300 reef-protected areas, of which the largest and most famous is the Great Barrier Reef Marine Park off the coast of Queensland, Australia.

Management of this reef system is based on a system called zoning, which attempts to reduce conflicts and minimize environmental

Above: Before he mates, the male cuttlefish will attract a partner through a courtship ritual in which he changes colour several times. A few hours after mating, the female cuttlefish lays her fertilized eggs among the corals.

Below: One of the greatest natural threats to the coral reef is the predatory crown-of-thorns starfish. It feeds on coral polyps and decaying vegetable matter, and a plague of these starfish can destroy large areas of reef.

Left: The giant clam is the biggest of all molluscs, growing to over a metre in diameter and weighing more than 200kg. It lies embedded in the coral, filtering water through its gills and feeding on the free-swimming algae that it traps in them.

damage by permitting specific activities only in designated areas. The Great Barrier Reef is fortunate in being large enough to incorporate preservation areas, but many other countries have smaller reef systems and rely heavily on tourism, with the result that their reefs are showing signs of over-use. Not only are corals damaged when visitors explore the reef, but the development of facilities to cater for their needs can be equally destructive. Education about the vulnerability of reefs is an important weapon in their defence.

The past decade has seen a decline in the health of corals on a global scale that is causing considerable concern. One of the most serious problems is the loss (or expulsion) of pigmented single-celled algae that live in the coral tissues. This happens when corals are stressed and is known as bleaching. It first occurred on a massive scale in the Caribbean in the early 1980s, but by 1987 had been reported from the Indo-Pacific. It is thought to be due to prolonged small temperature increases, and may be connected with global warming.

Bleaching normally leads to death of the corals concerned and significant changes to the reef ecosystem. If, as predicted, sea levels are set to rise as the oceans warm up, the dying-back of the corals could be disastrous. Low-lying island nations such as the Maldives are in danger of being partially inundated as a result of the rise in sea levels and could also become more exposed to severe flooding if they lose their barrier of living coral.

Corals are also affected by a number of diseases. One, known as white band disease, has seriously damaged a number of reefs in the Caribbean and is believed to be caused by bacteria. There have also been plagues of crown-of-thorns starfish, a species that preys on the living coral. The starfish have destroyed large areas of reef, and it is not yet known whether humans have played a part in causing this disruption of the balance of nature. Much remains to be learnt about this and other misfortunes that befall corals.

Elizabeth Wood

Opposite: There is nothing on land that can prepare divers for their first visit to the profusion of shapes, colours and teeming life that make up a healthy coral reef.

Below: When we interfere with the natural order by destroying coral reefs for our own purposes, such as this wall built from coral, we break the food chain and cause damage which may well have more lasting consequences than we realize.

POLES APART

The Arctic and especially the Antarctic are among the last great wilderness areas left in an increasingly populated and polluted world. There are signs of human influence even in these remote regions, but they remain largely as they always were — harshly beautiful places where wild nature still reigns. They are worth preserving for their own sake, but there is another and very practical reason for their conservation. They are like the miners' canaries of old, giving warning of environmental hazards to the world. Scientific information gained in these polar areas is essential in helping to maintain the planet as a home for both human beings and wildlife.

Humans have lived along the shores of the Arctic for thousands of years, subsisting on the natural riches but having a negligible effect on the environment. Nowadays these native people live mostly in modern settlements. By contrast, Antarctica was discovered less than 200 years ago when it had no native inhabitants. Today, however, it has a year-round population of around 1000, rising to 4000 in the summer.

Nevertheless, nature's riches have been heavily exploited in both north and south. The first animals to attract the hunters were the seals, especially the valuable fur seals. They were taken in huge numbers in both hemispheres, until the stocks had been almost wiped out and it was no longer economic to continue. Whales came next, first for their oil and then for their meat. Whaling came to end only when most species had reached such a low level that it was hardly worth going in search of them. At the same time, world opinion turned against the widespread slaughter and helped to bring about an almost total moratorium on commercial whaling.

Right: Antarctica contains about 90 per cent of the world's ice and 70 per cent of its fresh water. Only 2 per cent of Antarctica's land area is ice-free.

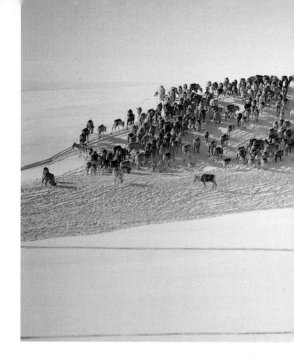

Right: Modern technology has made its presence felt in the Arctic, where snow scooters are used by the Lapps to round up reindeer herds. Technology has had a more adverse effect, too: in Norway the Lapps' reindeer are unfit for human consumption due to the fallout from the Chernobyl disaster.

A few small exceptions to the moratorium are made, under the designation 'aboriginal subsistence whaling'. Alaskan native people are allowed an annual catch of up to 41 bowhead whales, those in the Soviet Arctic a maximum of 169 grey whales, people living in west Greenland may take 21 fin whales and 115 minke whales, and east Greenlanders 12 minke whales.

Arctic fisheries have been relatively well controlled, largely because the oceans there are mostly within different nations' territorial limits. But in the Antarctic, where no country has sovereignty, it has been more of a free-for-all. Several species of fish in different regions of the Antarctic and sub-Antarctic have been heavily overfished in recent years. Each time a fishery has collapsed, attention has been focused on another stock in another place. The main species affected so far have been Antarctic cod and ice fish, and possibly squid. No one knows what effect this has had on the Antarctic ecosystem.

The next marine resource to be exploited was krill, the tiny sea creatures that support all marine and most terrestrial life in the region, either directly or indirectly. Krill are not especially palatable to humans, but are consumed in small quantities in Japan. Far larger quantities are harvested by the Soviets for use as supplementary feed for livestock. The krill fishery is causing concern, and needs very careful monitoring if stock levels are to be maintained.

Besides their biological resources, both the Arctic and Antarctic have mineral deposits of value to man. There is already substantial mineral extraction in and near the Arctic. One quarter of the oil produced in the United States comes from Alaska. But already the giant Prudhoe oil field is half exhausted. Northern Siberia accounts for about two-thirds of the Soviet Union's oil. In chilly Spitzbergen, Norwegian and Russian miners hack out nearly a million tonnes of coal each year. Nothing stands still in an energy-hungry world and exploration for oil and gas continues apace, especially in the Barents and Norwegian Seas, while Alaska's once sacrosanct Arctic National Wildlife Refuge may soon be opened for exploratory drilling.

Antarctica, too, may have commercially valuable mineral resources, but current

Below: Hungry polar bears turn their attention to a rubbish dump in Manitoba, Canada. Although they are primarily hunters, the bears will also scavenge if they have the opportunity, and may attack any humans they meet.

information on the occurrence, quality and likely quantities of deposits is sketchy and speculative. It is doubtful if extraction of any minerals would be commercially feasible at present — or worth the environmental risk. For example, the only iron and coal identified consists of some low-grade deposits in the Transantarctic Mountains, which are of no great interest. However, more interest has been shown in the Dufek Massif, which is geologically similar to the Bushveld Complex in South Africa where 85 per cent of the world's platinum is mined. But the site is largely ice-covered, is 550km from the nearest sea, and it is not yet known if significant mineral deposits might actually be found.

There is little definite evidence of major oil and gas fields in Antarctica, contrary to recent publicity, and no evidence that such resources, even if they do exist, would be commercially viable. Antarctica must be one of the most unfavourable places on earth from which to extract and transport oil. There is thick ice cover on land. The water offshore is deep, and in the most likely areas for finding oil there are vast jostling icebergs and dense pack-ice that would pose enormous dangers to oil rigs, tankers, pipelines and sea bed drilling installations.

Oil production in Antarctica seems a very long way off, yet the subject has been hotly debated inside and outside the Antarctic Treaty system. After much discussion, it was finally agreed in July 1991 to ban oil production (and other mineral extraction) in Antarctica for at least 50 years.

Despite this encouraging development, the polar regions do face a number of other threats. Pollution in particular is of immediate concern.

One of the most environmentally damaging oil spills of all time was caused by the *Exxon Valdez* tanker that went aground in Prince William Sound, Alaska, in March 1989. The 40 million litres of crude oil that leaked out killed nearly 400,000 seabirds, about 5500 sea otters, 200 harbour seals, and an unknown number of killer whales. At least 26 archaeological sites were seriously damaged and hunting and fishing by local people badly affected. The Exxon company was fined $100 million (approximately £59 million), the largest ever fine for a crime against the environment, plus $900 million (approximately £530 million) for the clean-up operation.

During the clean-up, much effort went into spraying 600km of beaches with high-pressure jets of seawater heated to 70°C.

Below: Although the Eskimos now live mostly in modern settlements, some of their traditional methods of hunting and fishing are still employed. These methods have allowed them to live in the Arctic for years without damage to the environment.

Above: The *Exxon Valdez* tanker caused one of the most environmentally damaging oil spillages of all time. A rescue centre was set up in Alaska to attempt to treat as many birds and mammals as possible. Here, a badly affected sea otter is cleaned by helpers.

Below: Sophisticated methods have been developed to deal with oil pollution. Here, a floating boom is used to clean up an oil slick off the coast of Alaska.

Unfortunately, this may have been more damaging than doing nothing since it has sterilized the beaches, killed marine life and changed the nature of the beaches themselves. American marine biologist Sylvia Earle commented that it would have been better to let nature take its course.

The Gwich'in people living on Alaska's north coast have called for a ban on oil exploration. They depend on the caribou herds that live in the area and, as one tribal elder said, 'Oil does not combine with living things. If the caribou go, we go.'

They are right to be concerned. In the Soviet Arctic, faulty equipment leaks a

million tonnes of oil on to the tundra each year. This, plus intensive traffic by lorries and other machinery, has damaged an estimated 2000sq km of reindeer grazing land.

Pollution at some Antarctic scientific bases has been quite severe, with solid and liquid wastes of all kinds carelessly dumped on land and, more damagingly, in the sea. Credit is due to Greenpeace, and also to tourists and other outsiders who visited the bases, for bringing this situation to light. Now, the scientists are starting to clear up their mess.

A major oil spill occurred in the Antarctic in January 1989, when the *Bahia Paraiso* went aground and sank, spilling 772,835 litres of fuel oil. The next breeding season proved disastrous for the Antarctic skuas in the area, but in this case the oil was not to blame. The breeding failure turned out to be part of a complicated natural cycle related to the weather. In fact, it resulted from especially cold winters in 1980 and 1981.

Another misconception was to blame the spill on tourism, which led to a widespread demand for strict controls, or even a ban, on Antarctic tourist cruises. There were some tourists on the *Bahia Paraiso* — but it was not a tourist ship. It belonged to the Argentine navy and was making its annual voyage to resupply Argentine bases (which was why so much fuel oil was on board).

The danger posed by tourism is very slight. About 3000–4000 tourists visit the Antarctic each year, which is a fraction of the numbers visiting the Arctic. Yet there have been no calls for banning Arctic tourism, although the marine ecosystems are quite similar. In fact, the Antarctic cruise operators have worked out a set of voluntary guidelines that are far more comprehensive and strict than those laid down by the Antarctic Treaty or by national legislation in countries like Britain and the USA.

All of the Arctic lands, and most of the Arctic seas, lie within national territorial limits, so in theory it is quite simple for the nations concerned to control what goes on, and thus to conserve resources and protect the environment. But in the Antarctic, where no country has sovereignty (though several, including Britain, have lodged claims), it is a different matter. To overcome this lack of authority, the 12 nations active in Antarctic scientific research signed the Antarctic Treaty in 1961. Altogether some 38 governments, representing 80 per cent of the world's population, have now acceded to the treaty.

The Antarctic Treaty covers all land south of 80°S, but the surrounding oceans are covered by various international rules and regulations, such as the Law of the Sea. The treaty bans actions of a military nature, and aims to curb pollution, avoid duplication of research, and conserve wildlife and other natural resources. It is often cited as a uniquely successful international agreement.

The reality, however, is somewhat different. It has failed to curb pollution, and has achieved little to control overfishing and disturbance of wildlife. The central problem is that to preserve harmony — which is essential to the smooth functioning of the treaty — the parties are reluctant to criticize each other. For example, construction of an airstrip at the French Dumont d'Urville station destroyed the breeding sites of many seabirds. This caused an international outcry when it was publicized, but it was left to Greenpeace, a non-governmental organization, to do so.

Enormous disturbance was caused to a large Adelie penguin rookery near the Argentine Esperanza station by the repeated low-level overflights of a helicopter. This resulted in widespread panic, leading to abandonment of chicks and eggs. The event was witnessed by horrified passengers and staff on board a tourist ship, who duly reported it. Like the French action, it was a direct breach of the Antarctic Treaty's own provisions.

If the Antarctic Treaty nations do not greatly improve their self-regulation there are bound to be increased calls to replace this 'gentleman's agreement' with some kind of truly international authority, probably under United Nations auspices. Whether that would be any more effective is a matter of opinion.

The polar regions are vital for the scientific study of the earth's environmental systems. It was long-term research at the British Antarctic Survey's Halley station that identified the infamous 'ozone hole' over Antarctica. Destruction of the ozone layer has potentially catastrophic consequences for all living things. Atmospheric ozone is the only substance that can filter out the sun's ultraviolet-B radiation (UVB), which is fatal to life. But a wide range of other scientific studies is being carried out in Antarctica and the Arctic, all of which require a natural and, as far as possible, uncontaminated environment if they are to be effective.

Nigel Sitwell

Below: The sea otter is one of the most fascinating Arctic mammals to observe, as it is extremely dextrous with its front paws. Prey taken from the sea is almost always brought to the surface for consumption: here the otter is eating a sea urchin.

THE EUROPEAN ENVIRONMENT

Above: Changes in farm buildings have had tragic effects on wildlife. The barn owl has declined in number all over Europe as old-fashioned barns have been pulled down or converted into homes, depriving the owls of their customary nest sites.

Opposite: The Flow Country is the largest single area of bog in Europe. Ground-nesting waders such as the golden plover and the dunlin breed here in their thousands, and birds of prey such as the merlin and the peregrine falcon find ample prey on the bog.

Right: Largely as a result of EC subsidies, huge fields of yellow oil-seed rape dominate the countryside of northern Europe in early summer.

From the wild and desolate peat bogs of the Scottish Highlands to the sprawling wetlands of the Mediterranean, Europe boasts a wonderful heritage of wildlife and wild places. Over the past 40 years, however, much of the European landscape has been irrevocably altered by the huge increase in population and changing land use, brought on by the demands of agriculture and industrial development, the extent of which is quite staggering.

In Britain, 97 per cent of traditional meadows rich in wild flowers have been lost, converted into high-yield arable land and silage fields, and 50 per cent of our ancient woodlands have been cleared. In Greece and other southern Mediterranean countries, tourist and leisure developments have destroyed wetland habitats and disturbed marine mammals such as the loggerhead turtle and Europe's rarest mammal, the monk seal.

As the landscape has changed, some species have adapted and are able to thrive. The kestrel is a familiar sight in man-made open spaces such as motorway verges and

industrial wastelands, gulls find rich pickings on rubbish dumps, and birds such as the magpie and the starling find plenty to eat in urban and suburban areas, as do adaptable mammals such as the brown rat and the red fox. For the most part, however, Europe's wildlife has suffered greatly as the actions of humans have destroyed or modified its habitat.

The ever-encroaching tide of mechanized agriculture has had the most sweeping effects. Over much of northern Europe the countryside is laid out in a patchwork of vast single-crop fields, a result of the European Community (EC) Common Agricultural Policy (CAP). Under this policy, European farmers are subsidized for growing particular crops. Traditional mixed farms, where a variety of crops was grown in smaller fields, have largely gone, and with them many farming methods that actually benefited wildlife. As these have died out, semi-natural wildlife habitats, where many species of bird and butterfly found homes, have disappeared. The chough thrived in a habitat of low-intensity farming, particularly land grazed by sheep and cows, but this delicate balance of agriculture and nature has now gone and the chough has disappeared from much of Europe.

One bird in particular, the corncrake, is a tragic illustration of the effects of intensive farming methods. In late spring, returning from its wintering grounds in Africa, the corncrake builds its nest on the ground in hay fields. Traditionally, hay was harvested in late August, when the corncrake chicks were several months old, and a single field would

Above: The corncrake is a victim of modern intensive agricultural methods. There are now only around 6000 corncrakes left in western Europe, although in eastern Europe, where farming methods are less intensive, populations are much healthier.

Below: Traditional headlands (strips at the edges of fields left untouched by the plough) provide a vital refuge for many small wild creatures, but they are being eaten away by increasingly sophisticated machinery and agricultural practices.

take several days to cut. Nowadays, grass is cut for silage (fermented animal feed) much earlier in the year when the corncrake's eggs have barely hatched. In these days of mechanized farming, it takes only a few hours to cut a hay field and the usual method is to harvest from the outside inward in ever-decreasing circles. This allows the female corncrake and her young chicks no escape route. Nests and eggs are often sucked up the silage chute or torn to pieces by the rotary mower.

Less instantly visible, but more far reaching and deadly than the use of machinery, is modern farming's use of pesticides and herbicides. These are chemicals used to increase agricultural yields by protecting crops from insects and weeds. In the 1950s and 1960s, enormous quantities of chemicals were applied to crop seed and farmland all over Europe. Thousands of seed-eating birds died after eating poisoned seed and, as the birds were preyed upon by flesh-eating mammals such as the red fox, the death toll steadily spread up the food chain. The effect on European bird of prey populations was disastrous — the peregrine and sparrowhawk almost disappeared from many parts of northern Europe.

The use of these dangerous substances has now been banned within the EC. Pesticides and herbicides — albeit new and safer ones — are still heavily used, however, and while the effects are less devastating, they still disrupt the delicate balance of natural communities. As herbicides kill off weed plants, they remove suitable places for butterflies and other insects to lay their eggs and, as the insects decline, so do the birds that feed on them.

As agriculture has become more efficient and the demands placed upon it have grown heavier, more and more 'non-productive' land has been brought into production. All over Europe bogs, woodlands and wetlands have been cleared and drained and many beautiful wildlife habitats, including meadowland and heathland, have become part of one huge agricultural 'green desert'.

Peat bogs are particularly vulnerable. The Flow Country, one of the most spectacular of Europe's few remaining wild landscapes, extends for almost 4000sq km over the hills of Caithness and Sutherland in the far north of Scotland. This unique habitat of upland bog, moorland and open water provides a home for many specialized insects unique to the area, as well as breeding birds rarely seen in Britain.

The Flow Country is a unique and fragile habitat of international importance, but in

recent years it has been the victim of commercial destruction and exploitation. Encouraged by tax incentives, investors have drained and ploughed up the Flow Country to plant massive areas of conifer forest at a rate of about 4sq km per month. By 1988, around 640sq km of the 4000sq km of blanket bog had been destroyed. The tax incentive has now been removed, but the ploughing and drainage of this delicate habitat has caused the loss of all the waders and the disappearance of bog plants such as the yellow asphodel from the ploughed-up area. Ironically, the Flow Country is not even a suitable habitat for tree plantations. The thin peat soil retards growth, necessitating the use of large amounts of fertilizers, and high winds often blow down the trees.

Recently, another use has been found for the Flow Country. Having destroyed an enormous proportion of Britain's lowland raised bogs (bogs that swell up above the surrounding land, forming beds of peat as much as 9m deep), the peat industry has now turned its attention to the area. Peat is commercially 'milled' for gardens, permanently destroying the whole bog in the process.

The outcry over the destruction of the Flow Country has died down over the past few years as the immediate threat of afforestation has been reduced, and there is a risk that this wilderness habitat may suffer because it is not considered a great beauty spot, despite its environmental significance.

Considerable impetus is now coming from environmental groups such as Friends of the Earth towards finding practical alternatives to peat. Many well-known gardeners now recommend the use of substances such as coir dust, a by-product of coconut processing that is not only economical but just as effective as peat, and which is becoming more and more widely available in garden centres. If alternatives like this catch on, the destruction of peat bogs may be stemmed. It would be a tragedy if, now that there is some hope for the survival of the Flow Country, this unique wilderness habitat were to fall victim to the needless extraction of its lifeblood.

The wetland habitat also supports a myriad of specialized plants and wild creatures such as herons and other waders, wildfowl, dragonflies and a host of other insects that need moist conditions to survive. But drainage is not the only threat to these marshy habitats. The huge amounts of nitrogen fertilizers used in modern farming, together with nitrogen from sewage and

Above: The peregrine falcon, which dives spectacularly out of the sky to attack other birds, was one of the predators seriously affected by pesticides in the 1950s and 1960s.

Left: Drainage of the Fens in East Anglia led to a decline in milk parsley, which is the only plant on which the larvae of the British swallowtail butterfly feed. As a result, the British swallowtail is on the brink of extinction.

vehicle exhaust fumes, are washed off fields into rivers and streams and seep into rivers, lakes, estuaries and coastal waters, where the effects can be devastating, encouraging the growth of excessive algae that upsets the natural balance of oxygen in the water.

The North Sea, too, is a diverse and unique habitat. It is one of the largest shallow marine areas in the world and hosts a great variety of marine life — over 170 species of fish live in its waters, along with 30 species of whale and dolphin, 6 species of seal, and countless smaller animals such as starfish, sponges and shellfish. But it is for its populations of seabirds and waders that the North Sea is particularly valuable. Over 30 species, including puffins, guillemots, razorbills, gannets, cormorants and several species of gull and tern, breed on its fringes, and many species of wader spend the winter there.

Yet, after years of being used as a dumping ground for the discharges and waste products of industrial life, the North Sea and the wildlife that depends on it are gradually being destroyed. Pollution, including sewage, agricultural run-off, industrial chemicals and oil from oil wells and shipping, is the major hazard, but much of the North Sea is threatened in other ways. Already, many of the coastal wetlands that line its shores have been drained for agriculture or reclaimed for industrial development or waste disposal, depriving many wading birds of their habitat.

In the early 1980s, concern reached such a high level that political action was essential. The eight nations that border the sea met and agreed to reduce the discharge of toxic substances and nutrients and to cooperate in research into North Sea pollution. The third North Sea Conference, held in March 1990, agreed on further measures to reduce pollution, and seven of the states agreed that the North Sea is not a suitable dumping site for radioactive waste. Britain was the only dissenting voice. Unfortunately, targets set by the conferences have rarely been met and

Right: Gannets are just one of the many species of seabird that breed around the North Sea. Yet this environment is under threat after years of being used as a dumping ground for industrial discharges and waste products.

Right: Poisonous chemicals applied to crops have had a disastrous effect on the sparrowhawk. As the birds preyed on smaller birds contaminated by treated seed, poisonous residues built up in their bodies until finally their eggshells became so thin that they were broken when the birds sat on them. With the banning of many of these chemicals, the threat to the sparrowhawk has diminished, and numbers are now on the increase.

if the North Sea and its host of wildlife are to be saved, a lot more effort will be needed.

In the last few years, public awareness of environmental concerns has increased all over Europe and we are getting more enjoyment out of nature and the countryside. Awareness of the problems caused to the environment by our modern lifestyle is not, however, enough to halt the damage. Action must be taken now to preserve our rich wildlife heritage for the future.

Education is extremely important, but it is also time for us to rethink our lifestyles and to begin taking positive steps to reduce the damage we cause. In addition, we need to look at the way in which we use nature for recreation. In some places we are in danger of destroying the very wild places we are trying to preserve. In national parks like Dartmoor and Snowdonia, paths are eroded by millions of visitors every year and wildlife habitats can be inadvertently disturbed. Less responsible use of the countryside can cause even more damage — areas of sand dunes damaged by off-road motorcycles and four-wheel-drive vehicles, and moorlands disturbed by over-enthusiastic mountain-bike riders — and needs to be carefully regulated.

Some hope for the European environment is offered by the European Parliament. EC agricultural policies are currently being re-thought, and the possibility of taxes on fossil fuel use and a new road tax system are two proposals under debate in Strasbourg. It is only through a concerted effort from public and governments alike that we can ensure that the exploitation and destruction of our beautiful environment is halted.

Hanna Bolus

ECOGLASNOST IN EASTERN EUROPE

With the raising of the Iron Curtain, the full horror of years of environmental neglect in eastern Europe has become apparent to the West. Only now are official figures on the environment being released by eastern European governments, and they make grim reading. Years of heavy industrial output with few environmental safeguards have left eastern Europe with a legacy of poisoned water, smog-filled air, contaminated land and dying forests: 55 per cent of east German forests and 75 per cent of Polish forests alone have been damaged by the effects of acid rain. In Romania, 80 per cent of rivers are heavily polluted, the water from a third of Polish rivers is so corrosive that it cannot be used even by industry and, in the River Elbe in eastern Germany, 70 per cent of fish embryos have been found to have deformities caused by toxic chemicals.

This is an ecological nightmare, but there is hope for the region. In many eastern European countries, political reawakening has been accompanied by a flourishing popular green movement and more real official concern about the environment. In Bulgaria, political change was actually triggered by an environmental pressure group, Ecoglasnost, and in Hungary, popular outrage at plans to reroute the Danube, removing it from its floodplain and channelling it through asphalt-lined walls, contributed to the start of the revolution.

Sadly, however, the Danube scheme does now seem set to go ahead, mainly because so much money has already been spent on it by both the Hungarian and Czechoslovakian governments. There are, however, many conservation projects under way in eastern Europe that offer much cause for optimism.

In Bulgaria, a wildlife reserve at Lake Sreburna in the Danube delta shelters a tenth of the world's population of Dalmatian pelicans (a critically endangered species), along with four other species of bird endangered in Europe. Under the Communist regime, the reeds on the reserve were harvested and, like many wetlands all over Europe, it faced conversion into a fish farm, reed farm or water sports centre. Now it is a well-run and successful sanctuary.

Positive environmental initiatives and good intentions will not be enough, however, to rescue the wildlife habitats of eastern Europe from the legacy of years of unbridled ecological abuse, and there is also the risk that, in attempting to emulate the capitalist systems of the West, eastern European countries will incur the same problems of overdevelopment. Furthermore, the West needs to make amends for years of using eastern Europe as a dumping ground for the toxic by-products of its own industries. Perhaps this should take the form of financial aid and advice, and the technology needed to clean up eastern Europe so that it is no longer one of the most polluted and dangerous areas in the world.

Below: The European bison conservation programme in Poland's Bialowecza National Park is just one of the projects now under way in eastern Europe.

THIRD WORLD ECOLOGY

The countries of the Third World stretch in a wide band around the globe, through Asia, Africa and Latin America. The most publicized of the concerns of conservationists are focused on conditions in these countries, where, despite fearful depredations, there are still large communities of wild creatures and extensive regions of wild terrain. Sometimes Third World countries are called Less Developed Countries (LDCs), to differentiate between them and the wealthy industrialized nations such as the USA, Japan, and the countries of Europe.

The people of the Third World live predominantly in rural areas, and a large proportion of them exist close to the poverty line. What distinguishes them above all else from their First World contemporaries is their disproportionately small use of the world's wealth. The planet's resources are sufficient to feed, clothe and house all its human inhabitants, despite the mind-boggling population increases of recent centuries. However, that could become a reality only if all the people on earth had equal access to its resources. An American, Japanese, Australian or British family, with its electrified house, family car, handy local supermarket, annual holidays, fashionable clothes, and access to health-care, uses up many times the resources consumed by its equivalents in India, Mozambique or Brazil. It has been calculated that a single Swiss consumes some forty times as much of the planet's resources as a single Somali.

Many of the ingredients of the affluent industrialized lifestyle come from the Third World, in the form of exports such as

Right: Although the tourist trade is lucrative, dead elephants are worth as much to villagers in Zimbabwe and South Africa as the magnificent herds of living ones. Governments still export ivory, and the local people receive meat and bone fertilizer from culled animals, so conservation methods may well be fatally flawed.

Above: If conservationists do not like the elephant schemes operated by African governments, then they must come up with viable alternatives that take human need into consideration as much as they do concern for these animals' welfare.

Below: The greatest threat to Zimbabwe's black rhinoceros population did not come from the country's own people, but rather from Zambian poaching gangs that came on raids across the Zambezi River.

minerals, timber and agricultural products. However, instead of becoming wealthy on export earnings, the Third World countries are in debt to the governments and banks of the First World. Exporting companies are often foreign-owned, and profits from home-owned companies are frequently siphoned off by the small ruling élite.

Many Third World governments have accrued vast international debts in the vain attempt to build an industrial infrastructure which has often been inappropriate to the needs of mainly rural populations. The debts increase after the failure of the investment, as interest payments continue to mount up. Africa as a whole receives foreign aid equivalent to $14 billion (approximately £8,240 million) annually, but has a debt repayment bill of $21 billion (approximately £12,400 million) annually. Sometimes the loans are for non-productive schemes, such as arms purchases — $6 billion (approximately £3,500 million) of Africa's annual 'aid' is for arms. Lenders such as the World Bank, and individual governments such as Japan, Britain and the USA, have an overriding interest in loan schemes that will make profits. Third World borrowers have to cut back on welfare programmes and other non-profitable operations in order to make the books balance to the lenders' satisfaction. Many of the schemes which First World

lending agencies have been willing to fund have been both inappropriate to the real needs of Third World countries, and damaging to wildlife and the terrain which sustains it. Large-scale dam projects are one example. Designed to produce hydroelectric power and service advanced irrigation schemes, huge dams destroy thousands of square kilometres of animal and human terrain, and disrupt the natural irrigation of annual flooding. The World Bank has been involved in over 400 such projects in developing countries in the last 40 years, and in recent years Japan has emerged as the single largest national investor, with a particular fondness for dams.

Agribusiness schemes are another favourite of the international lending agencies. Because they are basically concerned with single, large-scale crops, they often destroy small-scale mixed village farming, as well as damaging wildlife through their massive use of pesticides and artificial fertilizers.

Intensive cotton-growing, funded by foreign banks and agro-chemical concerns, has recently been instituted in the Zambezi valley in Zambia, displacing, for the second time in one generation, tribal peoples who were first moved from their traditional territories by the building of the Kariba Dam. This chemically nurtured cotton will severely undermine the operations of Zambia's small-scale cotton farmers, hastening the migration of rural dwellers to the towns, where bread riots have pushed a bankrupt administration further into debt in recent years.

It is significant that one of the greatest threats to Zimbabwe's black rhinoceros population has come from Zambian gangs raiding across the Zambezi. The lesson must be that sustainable conservation has to include a proper concern for the welfare of human as well as animal populations. Displaced and poverty-stricken people have one pressing motivation — their survival and that of their families.

All too often the administrations that apply for international loans for Third World countries are 'urban-minded'. Development and growth for their economies are seen in terms of cities, with their needs for transport systems, electrical power and industrial enterprises. Small rural communities, although they may constitute the majority of the population, tend to have their special needs neglected, and may be seen as 'backward', and be encouraged to 'modernize', although this inevitably entails increased migration from their homes to already overcrowded and underserviced cities. The lending agencies in their turn can see little profit in modest rural enterprises designed to increase self-sufficiency at the village level, though there may be far more need for such schemes than for hydroelectric dams or super highways.

Overleaf: Ivory is still taken from culled elephants. On 20 June 1991, Botswana, Malawi, Namibia, Zambia and Zimbabwe signed an agreement to establish the Southern Africa Centre for Ivory Marketing. Under this agreement, elephant ivory will be marketed through a single centre.

WORLD POPULATION GROWTH

The growth of the world's human population has been remarkable over the last few centuries. At the time of Christ, when the first water wheel was in use, there were perhaps 300 million people on earth. This had risen slowly to about 500 million by the middle of the seventeenth century, when Galileo invented his telescope. By the time of Stephenson's Rocket *locomotive, in the middle of the nineteenth century, the figure was over 1 billion. Less than a hundred years later 2 billion was reached. There were 4 billion by 1975, and there will be over 6 billion people*

on earth by the end of the twentieth century, consisting of 1.3 billion in the developed world, and some 4.8 billion in the developing countries (symbolized here by the space shuttle and the dam respectively).

The growth of preventive medicine, including vaccination campaigns, is responsible for much of the surge in Third World populations. Another cause is the move from rural areas to cities. Traditionally, land could support as many people as it could adequately feed, but more people can be crammed into cities. The urban

population of developing countries rose from 295 million to 1.3 billion between 1950 and 1988. Poverty, too, is a contributor to population growth. The poor often consider children to be a form of security, and are less likely than the rich to have access to adequate birth-control advice and facilities. While complaining about Third World population growth, the First World spends a mere $1 billion (approximately £600 million) a year on family planning programmes for developing countries. Three times that amount would be insufficient.

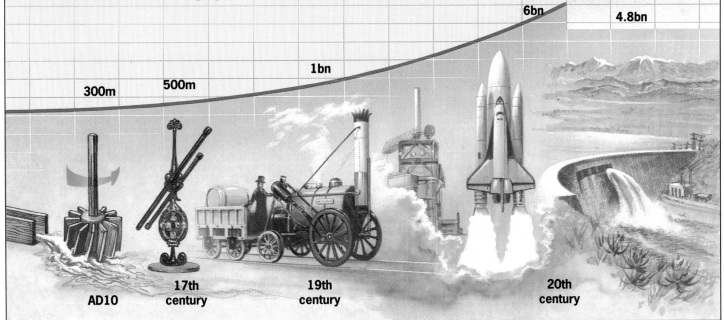

300m — 500m — 1bn — 6bn — 4.8bn

AD10 — 17th century — 19th century — 20th century

Right: These South African rangers have successfully caught two poachers red-handed with a snared impala. But poaching remains a lucrative business, and because the likelihood of capture is still remote in many areas it still seems a risk worth taking.

Below: Many of the ingredients of an affluent, industrialized lifestyle come directly from the Third World, in the form of minerals, timber and agricultural produce. So it is the poorer regions of the world that are, in fact, sustaining us — and not the other way round.

The conflict of interests that exists between humans and wildlife can be clearly seen with regard to the Asian elephant, which many villagers regard as a threat to crops and homes. Much of the habitat of the Asian elephant in India lies in heavily populated areas. Deprived of adequate foraging areas, herds of elephants regularly raid crops and kitchen gardens. They come into frequent direct confrontation with the villagers, who light fires, make noise and assault the elephants with stones, flaming missiles and ancient blunderbusses. Both elephants and villagers are injured and sometimes killed.

The Asian Elephant Specialist Group of the International Union for the Conservation of Nature and Natural Resources (IUCN) believes that the only workable solution in India may be networks of reserves connected by forest corridors. The isolated small reserve inevitably results in the starvation of elephants or raids on village plots.

The planners of reserves need to balance human needs against those of threatened animal species, and they also need to make conservation schemes self-financing. Funds from charitable organizations are no solution in the long run, and the developed countries, as well as those of the Third World, need to view wildlife as a resource like any other, if its conservation is to be sustained. As a resource, wildlife has to be protected, managed and also paid for.

Both Zimbabwe and South Africa are maintaining successful elephant populations through a combination of rigorously protected reserves, annual culling to maintain the health of herds, and an involvement of local human populations in the management schemes. In both these countries, numbers of African elephants were dangerously low at the beginning of the century, but they have since recovered considerably.

Many conservationists, however, feel that the Zimbabwean and South African methods are fatally flawed, because both countries sell the ivory from culled animals. In Zimbabwe, where the number of elephants in national herds total 57,000, the foreign exchange generated by such sales is a significant input to the national budget. The sales benefit local villagers, who receive much of the meat from culled animals, as well as fertilizer made from the bones. Income from sales of tusks and hides is used in part to buy agricultural equipment for local human communities.

If conservationists living in the developed world are unhappy with the solution employed by Zimbabwe and South Africa for their elephant schemes, then they must come up with alternative ways of making conservation sustainable. Any such alternative will need to include the welfare and cooperation of local villagers in its calculations, and it must also be capable of generating regular and renewable income. Safari parks catering to tourists and photographic expeditions are the best-known way of financing conservation, but not all reserves can or should be geared to tourist invasion.

Ultimately those in the First World who set a high value on the survival of Third World wildlife and natural habitats must be prepared to pay the high price of sustainability. Addressing the real needs of Third World human populations, rather than investing in short-term commercial gain, is a first essential step in the process.

Duncan Brewer

OPERATION TIGER

With tiger numbers down to around 2000 in 1972, from a turn-of-the century total of at least 40,000, the World Wildlife Fund (WWF) launched Operation Tiger, adding international funds and expertise to the money raised by national governments for tiger conservation. In India, nine reserves were created. Some support facilities, such as schools and health clinics,

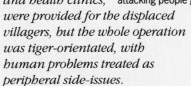

Above: This effigy gives tigers an electric shock to deter them from attacking people gathering firewood.

were provided for the displaced villagers, but the whole operation was tiger-orientated, with human problems treated as peripheral side-issues.

Until recently the statistics appeared to show that Project Tiger (India's scheme within the international Operation Tiger movement) was successful. By 1979 tiger numbers were up to 3000, and ten years later had reached over 4000. By 1990 there were 18

reserves. Today it appears that the extinction of India's tigers was only temporarily postponed, due to the failure of the conservationists to make adequate allowance for the human needs of local villagers.

Local populations have become alienated from Project Tiger. They graze their cattle and even cultivate crops within the reserves. Poaching is on the increase, and poorly paid forest guards are indifferent and ill-informed.

Current tiger numbers for all Indian reserves are under 1500. To resuscitate Project Tiger would require radical changes in the way staff are trained and paid, together with well-financed programmes to provide villagers with alternative fuels, such as biogas or solar heating, as well as the provision of extensive buffer zones around reserves, where domestic animals could be grazed.

Below: A tranquillized tiger can be studied and tagged for research.

THE POLLUTION
OF WAR

At 10 a.m. on 21 February 1991, Iraqi troops began one of the most unnerving acts of environmental terrorism ever. They set fire to hundreds of Kuwaiti oil wells, unleashing on the planet one of the largest palls of smoke seen in recent centuries. Scientists at Imperial College, London, looking at satellite pictures, saw the first smoke emerge from close to the Burgan oilfield in central Kuwait that morning. By 4 p.m., smoke billowed from the Sabriya field to the north and, by 7 p.m., yet more was coming from the nearby Rar Rawdatyan field. Kuwait was ablaze.

It was more than a month before western firefighters extinguished the first blaze, after the war was over. They warned that it could be more than a year before the fires, like giant Bunsen burners in the desert, were put out and the great black clouds engulfing Kuwait would disappear.

Within days, thick clouds of black smoke stretched for 600km down the Gulf towards the Strait of Hormuz, where the smoke finally dispersed on the winds and spread as a grey haze across the Indian Ocean. Over Kuwait, on some days, the dense smoke created a 'darkness at noon', when temperatures were as much as 10°C below normal. In Bahrain, 500km away, smoke clouds caused temperatures to fall by up to 3°C.

The burning fires gave off toxic gases such as carbon monoxide and hydrogen sulphide in such quantities that firefighters were made unconscious and had to be dragged away by colleagues. They posed a serious health risk, too, to people exposed to the smoke clouds. Kuwaiti doctors said that many young,

Right: The world may never have seen 'environmental terrorism' on a scale to compare with that ordered by Saddam Hussein and carried out early last year by his Iraqi troops, seeking to prevent the allied recapture of Kuwait.

days. Even so, there were days when most of Saudi Arabia was covered by smoke.

But the longer the fires burn, the more likely long-range effects become. By mid-summer, a thin layer of soot covered the Zagros Mountains in southern Iran and black snow fell in the Himalayas.

Above: To some more sceptical observers, the Gulf War was little more than a battle for control of some of the world's most significant oil supplies. The damage that the conflict caused the environment, and the staggering extent of the consequent wastage, must certainly render us all losers.

elderly and frail citizens were suffering from lung complaints. Asthma sufferers in cities 3000km away were especially at risk when the winds carried to them the smoke clouds which contained high concentrations of lung irritants such as ozone and sulphur dioxide. The nearest available comparison appeared to be with the 'pea-souper' smogs that once afflicted British cities.

Scientists estimated that the fires were producing gases responsible for acid rain at a rate similar to all the power stations in Britain put together. Rain 'comparable with the acidity of some highly polluted rainfall events in Europe' was likely, said Britain's Meteorological Office. It could be 'capable of inflicting damage on some sensitive crops'.

Early warnings that the smoke could reach the stratosphere, upsetting the ozone layer, blocking out sunlight and disrupting the world's weather systems, proved wrong. The smoke stopped rising at around 5km. This is well short of the ozone layer and low enough for the smoke to be 'rained out' or scattered by surface winds within a few

Astronauts aboard space shuttle flights reported seeing an unusual thin haze across the entire planet. Scientists believe that this may be a mixture of smoke from the Gulf fires and ash from Mount Pinatubo, the Philippines volcano that erupted in June 1991. Scientists at the Meteorological Office in Britain, who flew through the smoke in a research plane, plugged their measurements into computer models of the climate and concluded that the early prediction of a failure of the Asian monsoon rains was unlikely, but that 'there would be a possibility of increases in certain regions'.

Below: It is estimated that 735 oil wells were set on fire during the Gulf War. Almost a year later, very nearly half of them were still burning fiercely.

Above: Many thousands of cormorants and numerous other species of seabird were among the biggest and most visible wildlife casualties of the Gulf War. But an enormous list of mammals, fish and species of smaller, unseen, marine animals needs to be added to this toll of death.

Already there has been unusually heavy rainfall in Iran during March, which flooded hundreds of villages. And within weeks of the warning, record rains were bringing widespread floods further downwind, in both China and India. Nobody will ever know for certain, however, whether the Gulf smoke was to blame.

Firing the Kuwaiti oil wells was not the only act of environmental sabotage perpetrated by the Iraqi forces during the Gulf War. We now know that the oil slick that leaked into the Gulf when Iraq bombed tankers and terminals contained about 8 million barrels of oil — twice the world's largest previous oil spill, which occurred a decade before in the Caribbean. In a massive operation costing about $150 million

(approximately £88 million), the Saudi government had, within a few months, siphoned a quarter of this from the Gulf waters and cleared as much again from beaches. On the Karan Island, a key summer nesting place for the green turtles of the Gulf, conservation workers scooped thick black oil from three-quarters of the beaches before the turtles arrived. Sea mammals such as dolphins and dugongs have kept away from the slicks, according to the World Conservation Monitoring Centre in Cambridge, and only a handful have died.

The Saudi clean-up team also started to remove a carpet of oil and tar, often several centimetres thick, from 400km of coastline, where it had polluted important habitats for wildlife such as saltmarshes, mudflats and mangrove swamps. But many months later balls of tar as big as golf balls were still coming ashore in large numbers. Key sites such as desalination works and important wildlife areas have been cordoned off by the Saudis with rubber 'booms' that float on the water's surface. Tar balls often stay below the surface, however, and booms cannot prevent them from reaching the beaches. The Saudis hope that, with the worst of the oil removed, the natural ecosystems can recover. The tar balls will eventually sink to the sea bed. The sea itself will help. While the Gulf has only sluggish tides, the oil on the water will eventually be flushed out into the Indian Ocean, where sunlight and seawater will destroy it.

Up to 30,000 birds, mainly grebes and cormorants, became covered in oil and died on the beaches of the Gulf in the months after the war. Without the clean-up the figure would have been much higher. Many more birds are being trapped in the huge pools of oil that have formed around sabo-taged oil wells. Confused by these black desert oases, the birds mistake the oil for water. Ornithologists warn that some of the

millions of birds that stop for a few days on the Gulf mudflats during their migrations may die in flight because the oil that sticks to their plumage slows their flying.

Oil is by no means the only pollution to have been left behind by the fighting. In the aftermath of the Gulf War, Bedouins and their camels face trekking through a desert that is peppered with unexploded mines and

Above: The oil slick that leaked into the Gulf when Iraqi aircraft bombed Kuwaiti oil terminals was estimated to be twice as large as the world's previous biggest spill. About 4 million barrels of oil were siphoned from the waters and cleared from the beaches within a few months of the conflict's end.

Left: There is no doubt that, without the huge, multi-national clean-up operation that followed the end of hostilities in the Gulf, the effects of the conflict on wildlife and the whole environment would have been even more widespread and catastrophic.

Above: The detergents needed to break down an oil slick can have their own harmful consequences on the environment. It is not really much consolation following a tragedy on this scale, but at least oil is organic in origin and so will, slowly and eventually, be broken down by marine organisms.

Right: No one really knows what will be the long-term effects on the natural environment of having hundreds of thousands of troops living and fighting over many kilometres of previously uncontaminated desert sand.

the debris of war. And they may face an increase in dust storms that could last for several decades, according to an Egyptian-born geologist, Farouk El-Baz. He warns that, within a few weeks, tanks destroyed a crust on the desert sands that took hundreds of years to form. As the wind whips up loose sand, he predicts there will be 'a new generation of sand dunes marching southward' through Kuwait and along the coast of the Gulf for hundreds of kilometres.

The hundreds of thousands of Allied troops who were stationed in the north of Saudi Arabia created a massive amount of waste oil and sewage, much of which poured directly into the sand. It could pollute natural underground stores of water laid down beneath the desert in wetter times. In a country desperately short of water, this may be the longest-lasting environmental legacy of all.

Fred Pearce

POLLUTION IN THE PERSIAN GULF

Environmental damage in war is not new. In the Vietnam War, US forces destroyed huge areas of rainforest when they sprayed the herbicide Agent Orange from planes to winkle out guerrillas hiding in the jungle. During the Sino-Japanese War in the late 1930s, Chinese generals broke dykes and moved the course of the Yellow River hundreds of kilometres to the south in an effort to hold back advancing Japanese soldiers. As a result they drowned almost a million

of their own citizens, and engineers did not force the river back into its old bed for almost a decade. But the actions of Iraq during the Gulf War in 1991 number among the worst instances of what George Bush, the American President, dubbed 'environmental terrorism'.

The oil that has been poured into the sea is being cleaned up, but is still a real problem. The waters of the Persian Gulf move in an anti-clockwise direction (shown by the arrows), and it

takes over five years for polluted water to flush through the narrow Strait of Hormuz. While oil pollution from the war is in the water, winds and tides push the slicks further south along the shore of Saudi Arabia, towards Bahrain. This area is rich in valuable habitats — mangrove swamps, areas of coral reef and seagrass — where herons and flamingos feed, dugongs and turtles thrive, and ospreys, cormorants and terns nest. It is critical that this vital area is not destroyed.

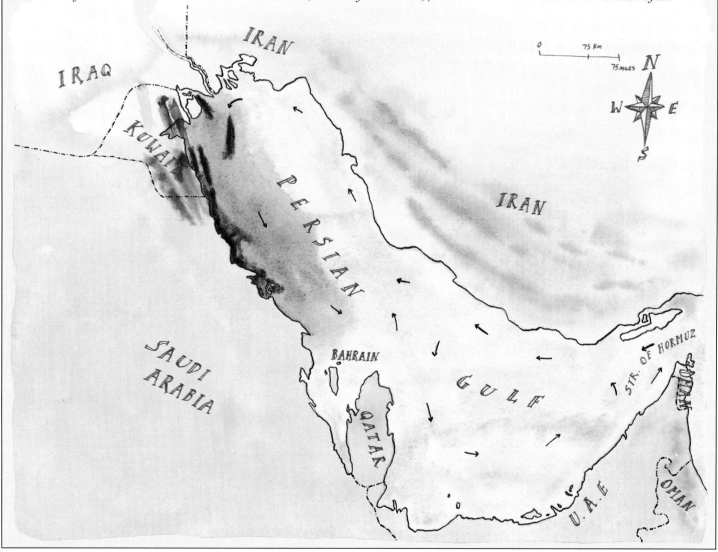

THE POLITICS OF WATER

When Jawaharlal Nehru opened India's first giant dam, the Bhakra Dam, in 1963, he called it: 'the temple of modern India, where I worship'. Like other leaders of independent nations — such as Nasser in Egypt with his High Aswan Dam on the Nile, and Nkruma in Ghana with his man-made Lake Volta — Nehru saw his shining new dam as a symbol of national independence. The dams would irrigate fields and generate massive amounts of cheap hydro-electricity. They would catapult their nations into the industrial age. A generation later, in the spring of 1991, demonstrators in India went on hunger strike to prevent the construction of the latest super-dam in the centre of their country, the Sardar Sarovar dam on the Narmada River. Baba Amte, a veteran fighter for the poor, said: 'All those ruthless, monstrous projects Nehru called temples of development have become tombs of development.'

Below: Construction has now begun on the Sardar Sarovar Dam in Gujarat, which forms part of the biggest multi-dam scheme in the world. The Indian government expects the dam to provide 68 billion litres of water daily, but critics claim that many of the villages in Gujarat will derive no irrigation benefits from it. Much fertile farmland will be destroyed in the Narmada Valley and the habitat of many rare animals will be lost.

Today, in many countries, big dams are seen as environmental and human disasters. The Sardar Sarovar, the first of a series of dams planned for the Narmada, will submerge thousands of hectares of forest — forest that forms the habitat of tigers, wolves and hundreds of rare species of reptiles, amphibians and plants. Drowned too will be the homes of tens of thousands of

poor farmers and tribespeople. The people's livelihoods are to be sacrificed to provide water and hydroelectric power, largely for industrial cities in neighbouring states. As construction progressed, the first villages were flooded in the summer of 1991.

Today, more than a tenth of the world's major rivers are dammed. Their waters are held in huge reservoirs, some holding tens of cubic kilometres of water, ready for release through turbines or canals when engineers and politicians decide. The natural flood cycles of the rivers are destroyed. Forests and underground stores of water in the rivers' floodplains dry out. Silt that once fertilized fields and maintained river deltas is now trapped uselessly on the bottom of the reservoirs.

Above: Africa suffers from acute water shortages, with less than 2000 cubic metres of water per person per year in much of the country. The water level has fallen visibly in this West African river.

Above: The first stage of the James Bay hydroelectric scheme in the 1970s cost a total of Canadian $15 billion (approximately £7,650 million), and was intended to make Quebec self-sufficient in its energy requirements. It severely damaged the livelihood of the Cree and Inuit people of northern Canada, and water released from one of the dams drowned 10,000 caribou. Work has now begun on the second stage of the project.

the islands, tiny groups of animals, isolated when the reservoir filled, gradually die.

Governments of all political persuasions love grand designs to remould their lands. In the Canadian Arctic the state government of Quebec wants to transform its rivers — in this case to generate massive amounts of hydro-electric power. In 1991 work began on James Bay II, the second stage of a mammoth project to capture the rivers that flow into the

But economists have never attempted to balance the costs of this natural disaster against the 'benefits' of their giant structures. The result is growing conflict with governments, hungry for power and water, pitted against the people who lose their forests and see their homes and fields flooded or their wells dry up. In northern Nigeria, for instance, 300 farmers were killed when they fought police to prevent the completion of the Bakalori Dam, which flooded their land.

In Brazil, the Balbina Dam, completed two years ago, flooded an area of Amazon rainforest the size of an English county to create enough electricity to run a medium-sized town. Forest land the area of 25 football pitches is flooded to generate enough power to run a 1-kilowatt electric fire. The reservoir is so shallow that, says Philip Fernside, a veteran Amazon researcher, 'from the air, you can see brown trees beneath the water over huge areas. A third of the reservoir is less than 4m deep and breaking the surface are 1500 islands.' On

James and Hudson Bays and divert them through turbines to generate hydroelectricity. James Bay I, built in the 1970s, destroyed fisheries and traplines, ending the traditional way of life of many Cree and Inuit people. Water released from one of the project's dams drowned 10,000 caribou, the North American version of reindeer. James Bay II, for which preparatory work such as road-building began in 1991, may force the beluga whale

out of Hudson Bay. The Cree, who accepted a £225 million cash settlement to allow James Bay I to go ahead, say they will fight to the bitter end to prevent James Bay II.

Big dams threaten to spark off international as well as local conflicts. A flashpoint for war in the Middle East is the River Jordan. In the 1960s, Israel diverted much of the river's flow away from the parched country of Jordan, pouring it instead into its

Below: The problem of water shortage is not confined to the Third World, especially as the demands for it in developed countries are so much greater. Nowhere is this more true than in the United States of America. This is the Fontana Dam, situated in the Great Smoky Mountains.

Right: Government policies towards nomadic herding communities may cause damage to water supplies. Attempts to settle nomads and prevent their migration by digging deep wells for their cattle can dry up shallow wells and water holes in the surrounding area, as well as causing cattle to overgraze their pastures.

Above: Irrigation can have a spectacular effect on the fertility of desert soil. Saudi Arabia now grows wheat and even rice amid the sands of the desert, thanks to giant pumps tapping underground water. These supplies are irreplaceable, however, and heavy demand on them has the effect of lowering the water table.

own national water grid. One result of the diversion is that the coastline of the Dead Sea, into which the River Jordan drains, has retreated, making the waters even more salty. Any resolution of the political disputes in this region will require an agreement about the fate of the Jordan's waters.

Another dispute that could lead to war is over the River Euphrates. Turkey is currently diverting the river's headwaters into the giant Ataturk Dam. It wants to use the water to irrigate fields. Downstream, countries like Syria and Iraq are already short of water.

India and Bangladesh are at loggerheads since India built the Farakka Barrage on the River Ganges. It prevents half of the dry-season flow of the river from spilling over the border into Bangladesh. The diverted water helps keep the waterway to Calcutta port free of silt, but in Bangladesh fields dry up and salty seawater infiltrates tens of kilometres, destroying crops.

Egypt, which depends on the River Nile for most of its water, crops and electricity, is apprehensive that its upstream neighbour could divert the river. Three-quarters of the water comes from Ethiopia, which wants to harness the Blue Nile. Boutros Ghali, an Egyptian foreign minister, said in 1990 that defence of the waters of the Nile was the one issue which could take his country to war. For the future, Egypt is tapping 'fossil water' laid down beneath the Western Desert thousands of years ago when the Sahara Desert was wet and many other rivers as large as the modern-day Nile flowed through it.

Similar strategies are being adopted in other Middle Eastern countries. Saudi Arabia now grows wheat and even rice amid the sands of the desert, thanks to giant pumps tapping underground water. In 1991 Libya finished the first stage of its Great Manmade River Project to pump water from beneath the desert through giant pipes for hundreds of kilometres to coastal farms. The scheme, which is using billions of dollars of oil revenues, aims to make Libya self-sufficient in food and secure its long-term future after the oil runs out.

In the future, exploitation of groundwaters, the great stores of water in rocks beneath the ground, will become increasingly important. Already in many countries, notably Saudi Arabia, the water table is falling fast, drying out wells and water holes used by animals. Sometimes the water is taken for city domestic supplies or industry, sometimes for plantations of thirsty crops, such as rice and sugar cane, which are often grown in deserts in Africa and India today.

But shortage of water is not exclusively a Third World problem. In south-east England, the overextraction of underground water resources to irrigate golf courses and supply new towns is causing springs to dry up each summer. As the springs fail, many rivers diminish to a trickle. In the dry lands of the American West, even large rivers such as the Colorado have so much water taken from them to irrigate farmland and supply big cities such as Las Vegas and Phoenix that they are almost dry in their lower reaches.

Half of Africa faces an acute water crisis during the 1990s. Other countries such as India are fast running short. Meanwhile, new technologies that can save water, especially for irrigating fields, go unused. The world's demand for water is rising rapidly, but ultimately the supply of water from rivers and underground water stores cannot be increased. Unless the world can dramatically increase the efficiency of its use of water — in homes, factories and especially on farms — then some predict that, before long, wars will be fought over water.

Fred Pearce

THE ARAL SEA

In central Asia giant dams divert so much water to irrigate cotton fields that the rivers dry up in some years. The Aral Sea, the great inland lake into which they pour, is less than half its size of 30 years ago. In places its shoreline has retreated by 100km through evaporation. Coastal forests around the Aral Sea where wild boar, tigers and deer once roamed are now desert and the huge fish stocks in the sea have all gone. The government calls it an 'ecological catastrophe', but a new dam was planned for 1991. If present rates continue, by the year 2000 the Aral Sea will have shrunk by another third.

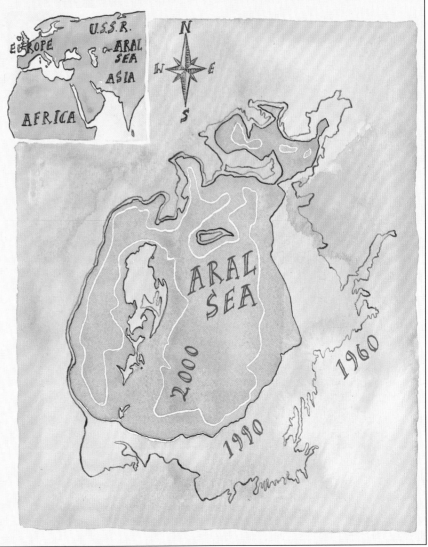

THE WILDLIFE TRADE

For centuries, humans have hunted wildlife, whether for food, pleasure or profit. Today, the trade in live wild animals and their products is very big business indeed, and the international agencies that seek to monitor and control trade in rare or endangered animals face a continual battle against human greed and indifference.

Hunting is an emotive issue. Romantic images of big-game hunters in Africa, or dashing English fox hunters, give hunting a veneer of respectability that belies the truth of its effects on wildlife. As the big-game hunters decorated the walls and floors of their homes with trophies of elephant tusks and tiger skins, populations of these animals, already dwindling with human invasion of their habitat, began their steady and irreversible decline.

Even today, hunting for pleasure is threatening the survival of some species. In several Mediterranean countries, such as Malta, Cyprus, Greece, Italy and France, hunters armed with semi-automatic shotguns take aim at the flocks of migrating birds that pass over each year *en route* from northern Europe to their wintering grounds in Africa. It is estimated that 2–3 million migrating

Above: Although governments may be persuaded to pass legislation forbidding the hunting and trading of endangered animals, stopping the practice of illegal poaching is another matter. Smugglers use ever more extreme methods to flout the law. So lucrative is their market that they receive considerable help from corrupt officials.

human interests. The puma has suffered a history of persecution in both North and South America because cattle ranchers saw it as a threat to their livestock. The lynx has also been hunted by European farmers, and although the decline of both cats can be blamed mostly on human invasion of their habitat and hunting for the fur trade, persecution in the name of pest control has been a significant contributory factor. In Europe, even protected birds of prey such as the hen harrier and the red kite run the risk of being shot or poisoned by the game-keeper, who regards them as threats to his stock of game birds. In Thailand, snake populations are steadily declining as they are hunted to protect domestic cattle.

Hunting may play a legitimate role in conservation, however. In Pilanesberg National Park in Bophuthatswana home-land, South Africa, where there is a sustainable population of white rhinoceros, permits are sold every year for ten rhino-ceroses to be shot for sport by wealthy hunters. The money raised is devoted to conservation management in the park. Similarly, in the massive Luangwa valley in Zambia, local landowners run game farms mainly for tourists, charging them fees for hunting licences and safaris.

Projects such as this have proved successful in stamping out poaching in these areas by giving local people an interest in conserving their wildlife as an economic resource. However, in many of the national parks of both Africa and Asia, poaching of protected wildlife is still widespread and in some areas protected animals are being poached simply for food. In the African state of Gabon, locals depend heavily on gorilla and pygmy chimpanzee meat, even though it is illegal to hunt either animal under international wildlife law, and in the Serengeti National Park in Tanzania zebra are herded into snares, then killed and butchered for their meat. This is a problem

birds are shot every year by Maltese sportsmen alone, and several million more are trapped and end their days in captivity. Many of these birds, such as song thrushes and skylarks, are killed quite legally, but the hunters do not discriminate between common and endangered birds — in fact, the rarer and more magnificent the bird, the more highly it is prized for mounting and display in private collections. In 1990, 150 ospreys were shot in Malta and the peregrine falcon (the original Maltese falcon) has disappeared as a breeding bird on the island.

Many species have been, and still are, hunted where their presence clashes with

Left: Tourists who come to see animals like the cheetah bring much-needed funds for conservation to the Kenyan national parks.

Below: The populations of many Third World countries still believe in the healing powers of some extremely unlikely ancient medicines. Often, these are prepared from the bones or organs of endangered animals. Without a substantial programme of health education, attempts to ban the use of such medicines are interpreted as an attack on traditional cultures.

for the governments of these countries to tackle with some urgency.

Perhaps the most widely supported and strongest international wildlife agreement is the Convention on International Trade in Endangered Species of wild fauna and flora (CITES). This agreement, drawn up in 1975 with the signatures of only ten nations, incorporates three appendices which lay down controls and restrictions in the trade of certain species and their by-products. The first appendix stipulates a total ban on trade in species that are threatened with extinction and may be affected by trade, which is permitted only in very exceptional circumstances. Included in this list of species are the giant panda, both African and Asian elephants, all five species of rhinoceros, all four species of great ape, all species of lemur, many monkeys, some big cats, all the great whales and some birds of prey. Appendix II imposes restrictions on a list of species that are at risk of becoming endangered if trade in them and in their

products is not controlled. Under the agreement, a CITES permit must be obtained to import or export one of these animals. The appendix covers all other species of primate, dolphin and big cat as well as fur seals, some parrots, birdwing butterflies and many others. The third appendix

allows individual nations to impose the same restrictions on trade in species that, while not in danger worldwide, are threatened by the activities of hunters and traders in their own countries.

CITES is far from watertight, however. Although it now has 113 signatories worldwide, its implementation is entirely the responsibility of the member states and its success depends in most countries on the ability and inclination of customs officers to enforce its terms. Several signatory nations are notorious for flouting CITES and, needless to say, some of the countries that provide the biggest markets for live wildlife and illegal animal by-products have not signed the agreement. Wildlife smuggling is such big business that CITES officials face an impossible task in attempting to wipe it out. Some of the tactics of the smugglers include forging permits, disguising or mislabelling consignments of live animals or animal products and bribing officials to turn a blind eye. In this way, illegal trade routes for endangered wildlife are kept open, giving the poacher a continuing motive for killing or trapping.

The wildlife poachers have developed ever more extreme methods for obtaining their quarry as measures to prevent poaching have intensified. In Kenya, poaching is a matter of life and death, as wildlife ranchers operate a shoot-to-kill policy, but still animals are taken. In Kaziranga National Park in India, poachers have devised an ingenious method of killing greater one-horned rhinos. By hooking a long wire over a high-voltage power line and leaving the two ends about a metre off the ground, they can electrocute passing rhinos with an 11,000-volt shock. Measures against poachers and smugglers will never be effective until the markets for products such as rhino horn are eliminated. Much has been done in recent years towards this end. The international ban on the sale of ivory which came into effect in January 1990 has helped significantly, and diplomatic efforts to eradicate the demand for rhino horn have had great success in countries such as Yemen, Hong Kong and Macao. There are now only four countries where significant trade in rhino horn persists — China, South Korea, Thailand and Taiwan. In China and South Korea, it has been used for centuries in traditional remedies for fevers and other ailments. South Korea has not signed the CITES agreement and so imports rhino horn with impunity; China has signed, but nevertheless imports around 650kg every year — a figure which means the death of 260 rhinos. Thailand, another CITES signatory, actually charges a duty on the import of rhino horn, in flagrant disregard of CITES.

It is the fur and pet trades that provide the most depressing evidence of the weakness of an international agreement in the face of the ruthlessness and greed of the wildlife smugglers. Trade in the skins of the larger cats such as the tiger, jaguar and leopard peaked in the 1960s, with about 15,000 jaguar skins reaching the USA and Europe every year. This level of slaughter and trade had disastrous effects on species such as the

Below: Red-eared terrapins have been imported into Britain in their thousands in the last few years with the booming craze caused by the Teenage Mutant Ninja Turtle cartoons. But such crazes quickly die out again, leaving unwanted and neglected pets as the result.

Left: In many places, crocodile skin is still regarded as a highly fashionable material from which to make shoes, handbags and other accessories. While such a market continues to exist, the chances of preventing poachers from hunting and exporting crocodile skins must remain small, although most now come from farmed animals.

Below: It is a sad fact that the more unusual the animal, the greater is its novelty value as a pet. But the reason for a species being unusual is that it is either extremely rare or unable to survive in an alien environment, so trading in such animals is almost certain to end in their premature death and gradual extinction as a species.

clouded leopard and snow leopard, both of which are still seriously endangered. During the 1970s, public opinion and the listing of these species in CITES Appendix I did much to halt the trade. Even today, however, it is possible to obtain a coat made from the skin of one of the big cats. With protection of the larger cats, the greatest proportion of the fur trade switched to smaller cats, and in particular to South American spotted cats such as the ocelot, margay and Geoffroy's cat. In 1989, the ocelot and margay were added to CITES Appendix I — a reflection of the serious damage caused by hunting to populations of these species. Yet again, however, it is still possible to buy an ocelot coat in Greece, for example, and (for a high enough price) to obtain a forged export licence to get it out of the country.

A similar situation reigns in the pet markets of the world: if you are willing to pay a high enough price, you can obtain even the most seriously endangered of wild animals as a pet. The most notorious markets are in the Far East. In the animal markets of Bangkok and Jakarta, endangered primates such as orang-utans, macaques and gibbons are regularly offered for sale, concealed from open view in boxes and crates. An orang-utan can fetch up to $5000 (approximately

£3000), and will normally end up either in a private collection or used in the entertainment business. In these circumstances, the orangs are likely to live for only a few years, as they become unmanageable as they grow and are destroyed by their owners.

Methods of obtaining wild animals for the pet trade raise serious welfare questions, as well as concerns about the effects on wild populations. To obtain a baby primate, the mother usually has to be killed and indeed sometimes the whole family group, which rallies round to protect the young, has to be wiped out. For the baby, capture is just the beginning of a long and traumatic experience. It is estimated that 70–90 per cent of baby primates captured in the wild die before they reach a pet market. A similar story applies to many other creatures. Transportation in cramped conditions, with inadequate food and water, causes many animals to die of dehydration, starvation or just shock. The tortoise is an example of this high mortality rate: of the tens of thousands of tortoises that were exported to the UK every year, 80 per cent died in transit.

In order to stop this kind of activity, not only must CITES be more strictly applied, but the markets for exotic and unsuitable pets must be reduced. Many unusual animals simply do not survive as pets. Red-eared terrapins, imported into Britain in their tens of thousands in the last few years due to the Teenage Mutant Ninja Turtle craze, are a good example. Ignorance of the conditions required for keeping them and of their rate of growth has led to the dumping of terrapins in the countryside by owners no longer able to cope with them. Even exotic pets that are widespread and freely available, such as parrots and tropical fish, should be considered unsuitable if they have been captured from the wild, rather than bred in captivity. Of the 4 million tropical fish imported into Britain every year, over 95 per cent are taken from the wild and many species, such as colourful angelfish and butterfly-fish, are very difficult to maintain in captivity. If these wild specimens are taken by careless collectors, untold damage can be done to fragile coral reef environments.

The tourist trade is another outlet for the illegal activities of animal trappers and hunters. In countries like Indonesia, trinkets for sale in tourist markets include such items as teeth from Sumatran tigers and stuffed marine turtles — both species covered by CITES. In order to defeat the hunters and smugglers, it is crucial for public awareness to be raised. Illegal hunting is now declining and hunting methods are coming increasingly under public scrutiny, so that the major threat to many species previously at risk from hunting and trade is habitat loss and pollution. However, there is no room for complacency. Animals such as rhinos and elephants that are targets for poachers cannot withstand sustained hunting owing to their slow rates of reproduction. If endangered species are to stand a chance of surviving in this world of shrinking wild habitats and increasing pollution, hunting for profit and pleasure must stop.

Hanna Bolus

Below: Hunting baby primates is a particularly wasteful business as, in order to get at the young animal, its mother and other members of the family group usually have to be killed. Such destruction can hardly be considered worthwhile when almost all the young die before they can be got to market.

Left: An orang-utan exported from the Far East can fetch about £3000 on the black market. It will normally end up in a private collection or be used in the entertainment business. In such circumstances, it will live just a few years or be destroyed as soon as it grows to its adult size and becomes unmanageable.

THE WILD BIRD TRADE

Every year millions of birds are captured in the wild to be sold through the pet shops and markets of the world. This exploitation is threatening the very survival of some species and the treatment of the birds during capture and in transit is a great cause for concern. On 21 May 1991, the Royal Society for the Protection of Birds (RSPB), in association with the Royal Society for the Prevention of Cruelty to Animals (RSPCA) and the Environmental Investigation Agency (EIA), launched a campaign calling for an end to the importation of wild birds into the European Community (EC). EC law currently prohibits the trapping, trade or export of native wild birds, but allows imports. After the USA, the EC is the main importer of wild birds, with over 1.5 million imported every year from Africa, Asia and South America. Many of the species involved in the trade are becoming rarer in the wild, as their habitat is destroyed and trapping depletes existing numbers too rapidly for the birds to recover. According to the RSPB, more than 41 species of bird are directly threatened with extinction due to the pet trade, 30 of which are species of parrot.

Among the parrots, it is the macaws that suffer particularly badly. For one species, the beautiful blue Spix's macaw, conservation efforts have come

too late. After decades of trapping, there is only one known bird left in the wild in Bahia state, Brazil. Other species of parrot directly affected by the trade include the stunning scarlet macaw; the hyacinth macaw of Brazil (the largest parrot in the world); the African grey parrot and the palm cockatoo of New Guinea. Hundreds of other types of bird are also victims of the trade: hummingbirds, sunbirds, honeycreepers, hornbills, laughing thrushes, fairy bluebirds, owls, hawks, falcons, finches — the list is almost endless. Many of these birds are protected by the Convention on International Trade in Endangered Species (CITES), but, as with other CITES-protected animals, the pet

Right: RSPB statistics suggest that only a quarter of consignments of Fisher's lovebirds on sale in Hong Kong are still alive by the time they reach their destination.

smugglers have ways of disguising their contraband through forgery or bribery. Recently, in the Netherlands, several captive hyacinth macaws, which traders claimed were captive-bred, were DNA finger-printed (that is, samples of their DNA were analysed). It was found that they were not the young of the stated captive parents, but undoubtedly wild-caught birds. This case, encouraging though it is, represents a mere drop in the ocean when protected birds such as Gurney's pitta and the Bali starling, each with only around 30 surviving wild individuals, are still available in the world's less respectable pet markets.

TRAFFIC (Trade Records Analysis of Flora and Fauna in Commerce), set up in 1976 by the World Wide Fund for Nature (WWF) and the International Union for the Conservation of Nature and Natural Resources (IUCN), is a network organization which monitors the international trade in wild animals and their products. TRAFFIC has its headquarters in Cambridge and 14 offices worldwide in countries known to be key routes for the wildlife trade. It is a low-profile organization, often operating under cover to expose corruption, exploitation and illegal trading in wildlife.

One of TRAFFIC's main concerns is to monitor the effectiveness of CITES. Because enforcement of CITES depends wholly on domestic legislation

in particular countries, animal dealers are often able to get around CITES regulations by using ports where they know controls are lax. TRAFFIC has exposed many of these weak links around the world, revealing that within the EC Spain is a particular problem area. TRAFFIC's work has also identified the main markets for the products of the illegal fur and pet trades, recommending the countries in question to step up scrutiny at airports.

It is not only illegal trade that TRAFFIC works to expose. It also monitors how excessive legal trade affects wild populations and presses for stricter regulations. It was largely TRAFFIC's investigations into the ivory trade that led to the current moratorium. More recently, TRAFFIC has exposed shocking statistics in the trade in South American spotted cat and reptile skins and in the live bird and reptile trades.

TRAFFIC's work is invaluable in raising international awareness of the scale of wildlife crimes and exploitation and in providing

Left: Many major airlines now realize that involvement in the bird trade is bad for their image.

accurate data from which new and more effective measures can be developed in the fight against the wildlife traders.

The methods employed by bird trappers vary a great deal. To catch small birds, such as songbirds and hummingbirds, branches are coated with a sticky substance which prevents the birds from flying away. Large flocks of birds are caught in mist nets (fine-gauge nets made out of Terylene thread) or clap nets (pairs of nets, closed by pulling on a long thread). After capture, the birds are either stuffed into long thin bags made of woven bamboo so that they cannot move their wings, or packed into boxes with their wings bound to their bodies for transportation. Often their beaks are taped up. RSPB estimates that one in four birds dies during transport-ation or in quarantine and that up to 75 per cent (in the case of some particularly vulnerable species) of all wild-caught birds die before they reach a pet shop.

It was the discovery, at Nairobi airport in 1990, of a crate of 10,000 birds, 1300 of which were dead, that finally prompted the German airline Lufthansa to ban the shipment of any further wild-caught birds on their planes. Now 22 more major airlines, including British Airways and KLM, have followed suit, realizing that involvement in the bird trade was bad for their image.

Public opinion is one of the most effective weapons in the fight against the bird trade. Members of the public can take a positive step by writing to RSPB to ask for a Campaign Action Pack on banning the wild bird trade. If you wish to own an unusual bird, make sure that the species is not endangered and press the pet-shop owner for proof that the bird was captive-bred rather than wild-caught, explaining why you are concerned. If the bird is captive-bred, it will often have a close-fitting ring around one of its legs. It will in any case be free from disease and be used to domesticated conditions. Captive breeding could easily supply the pet trade with enough birds, removing the need to take beautiful and endangered wild birds from their natural habitats.

Above: Half of the world's 16 species of macaw are now in danger of extinction as a direct result of their popularity among bird traders.

Wildlife and Conservation Organizations

While shutting the occasional field gate or taking home our litter after a picnic is as close as many of us get to conserving wildlife, there are many organizations dedicated to doing just that. Increasing the general public's awareness, lobbying governments and industrialists, raising money and planning projects is a full-time, international operation involving many thousands of paid and unpaid full- and part-time workers.

This section analyses the work of some of the world's leading conservation organizations and pressure groups. It takes a look at the work they do, at what they are trying to achieve and how they go about achieving it. It asks whether confrontational and emotional campaigning approaches can be justified and whether these organizations are always right in the goals they pursue, and how wildlife campaigns affect local people.

Below: The poacher and gamekeeper may have very different motives, but the methods and tools of their respective trades have much in common. This cheetah has been shot with a tranquillizing dart so that it can be weighed.

Above: The tourist industry is a vital means of sustaining the continuing work of conservation organizations. A safari through African game reserves provides much-needed finance.

THE GREEN AGENDA

Above: Modern environmentalism might be said to have begun 30 years ago with the formation of the World Wildlife Fund (now the World Wide Fund for Nature) in 1961.

Opposite: Greenpeace has a reputation as perhaps the most militant environmental pressure group. With offices and members spread throughout the world, it has become well placed to affect the attitudes of millions.

The fight against the destruction of the world's wildlife has, in the last generation, turned green organizations such as the World Wide Fund for Nature (WWF) into household names around the world. Close on the heels of this first international conservation pressure group followed more radical organizations such as Friends of the Earth and Greenpeace, both of which were formed around 20 years ago and now have offices around the world. While Friends of the Earth first encouraged us to recycle old cans, bottles and paper and to save energy, Greenpeace's concern with the environment went as far as direct action on the high seas.

It began when Canadian protesters sailed a boat into the testing zone for an American nuclear explosion on one of the Aleutian Islands off the coast of Alaska. They eventually attracted enough publicity and support to at least succeed in driving the tests underground. They then turned their atten-

tion to harassing whalers across the Pacific Ocean. Their tactic was to 'bear witness' to the bloody slaughter, to manoeuvre rubber dinghies between the harpoon gun and the whale and to photograph the confrontation.

'We saw it as a media war,' says Robert Hunter, a Canadian journalist and early president of Greenpeace. 'Planet-wide mass communication gave us access to the collective mind of the species that now controls the planet's fate. I saw Greenpeace as a symbol from which we might affect the attitudes of millions of people towards the environment.'

Today, the organization is somewhat different. Having achieved a high profile, Greenpeace returned to environmental campaigns, but its marine surveying equipment remains amongst the best in the world. Both Greenpeace and Friends of the Earth are now sophisticated organizations employing highly respected scientists, and whose advice is widely sought, even by governments.

Along the way there have been great victories. It was Greenpeace that forced European countries to agree to stop dumping sewage and other dangerous wastes into the North Sea, and obliged British Nuclear Fuels to spend hundreds of millions of pounds cleaning up pollution from its Sellafield nuclear reprocessing plant.

Greenpeace has always been about changing public perceptions with simple dynamic images. It was not long ago that most of the world saw furs as a sophisticated fashion accessory, a highly desirable luxury. Animal rights campaigners grumbled, Friends of the Earth and Lynx struck a few blows for rare species of cat, but it was a Greenpeace poster that changed more people's minds than anything else. It showed a woman in high heels dragging a fur coat that left behind a trail of blood. The caption

Right: The WWF was launched with a six-page 'shock issue' of the *Daily Mirror*, which featured a large picture of a black rhino and her baby.

Fur coat with matching accessories.

The leg-hold trap. For animals that don't get strangled, beaten, gassed or electrocuted.

LYNX

Fighting the fur trade

PO Box 509, Dunmow, Essex CM6 1UH

read: 'It takes up to 40 dumb animals to make a fur coat. But only one to wear it.'

It was much the same with whaling. In the 1950s, Aristotle Onassis, pride of the international jet set and owner of the world's largest whaling fleet, took VIPs on board his luxury yacht to watch the slaughter. They sat at bar stools of whalebone and used footrests made from the teeth of sperm whales. On land, we fed our pets with whale meat and there was whale blubber in our margarine. But Greenpeace pictures of harpoon guns, of blood in the water and huge carcases being hauled aboard the whaling ships, changed all that. The largest creatures on earth have been given a brief reprieve.

As organizations like WWF and Greenpeace grow bigger, it can often be small independent campaigners and groups who make the biggest news in the green movement. Take Allan Thornton. A Canadian, he worked for Greenpeace in the 1970s, confronting the hunters who clubbed baby seals to death on the ice floes off Newfoundland each winter. Later, he set up the first Greenpeace office in Britain. But his greatest triumph came only a couple of years ago, long after he had left Greenpeace to set up his own small but militant outfit, the Environmental Investigation Agency (EIA).

Throughout the 1980s, poachers had been killing African elephants in unprecedented numbers. Perhaps a million died to feed the international demand for ivory to make everything from trinkets to piano keys. But somehow nobody noticed the slaughter. The WWF, which has traditionally dominated environmental activity in Africa, had a policy of supporting 'legal' elephant hunting and a legal ivory trade. Some of its advisers hunted elephants themselves.

The idea was that if there was a legal trade, the poachers could be kept out. It did not work. By the end of the 1980s, four out of every five tusks on the international market were poached and, after the ivory

Rich bitch.

Poor bitch.

If you don't want millions of animals tortured and killed in leg-hold traps don't buy a fur coat. LYNX

had passed through a long chain of shady middlemen, nobody could tell what ivory had been legally taken and what illegally.

Thornton had heard about an ivory-processing factory in the small Gulf state of Dubai, run by a Mr Poon from Hong Kong, the godfather of the international ivory trade. It had turned millions of African tusks into trinkets for sale in the Far East, where the Japanese were the biggest customers. Thornton knew that pictures were the key to exposing the factory. He arrived in Dubai with the cover story that he was making a film about trade and bluffed his way to a ride on a fork-lift truck on a trading estate in order to get a view over the high wall that surrounded Poon's factory. The result was

film that formed the core of three special reports about the slaughter of African elephants shown on ITN and sold all over the world. The factory responsible for the deaths of 100,000 elephants a year was closed.

It was a brilliant coup, but Thornton knew that the factory could set up somewhere else within a few months. His real target was the international ivory smuggling network — the trail of counterfeit customs documents, ships' manifests, unmarked trucks and gun-traders that took tusks from the national parks of Kenya, Tanzania and southern Africa to Poon's factories and on to the clearing houses and the gift shops of the Far East.

'It was necessary to uncover the whole trade: the people who ran it and those who

Above and below: Attempts to destroy illegal trading in ivory by encouraging a limited, legal trade failed. This pile of confiscated ivory, worth £3 million, comes from 3000 elephants and was burnt in Nairobi on 18 July 1989.

Above: Few people objected to the catching of tuna fish until it was discovered that trawling methods needlessly killed thousands of dolphins at the same time. The only tuna that can be guaranteed 'dolphin-friendly' are those caught using a rod and line.

had permitted it to flourish,' says Thornton. 'We didn't go public for a whole year. We didn't even tell other environmental groups what we were doing.' His investigations laid the trade and its practitioners bare. To the Poons were added the Pongs of Pretoria and other trading families. He discovered the corrupt army officers shipping tusks from national parks in Zimbabwe, and the South African intelligence operators who helped Renamo guerillas in Mozambique trade tusks for guns.

His evidence, when published in full in 1989, forced the WWF to end its support for legal elephant hunting and, within months, led to a worldwide ban on the ivory trade. It was a remarkable victory, which he has followed up with a detailed investigation into the brutal international trade in exotic pets such as parrots, which largely operates through countries with lax customs controls.

Sleuth work brought success, too, in saving dolphins. The deaths of thousands of dolphins in the nets of tuna fishermen was brought to the world's attention only after

Sam LaBudde from the Earth Island Institute in California got a job on a fishing boat in the Pacific and brought back grainy video film of the slaughter. The fishermen, knowing that the tuna spend their lives swimming beneath schools of dolphins and that the dolphins were relatively easy to find, herded them into their nets in order to catch the tuna. After the video was shown round the world, public opinion quickly caused supermarkets in both the USA and the UK to state that they would accept only tuna caught by methods which would not harm the dolphins. To date, three-quarters of the canning firms have complied with the requirements.

Saving wildlife from hunters has been a major task for environmental organizations over the past 30 years, but it is only part of the story. Pollution, even in tiny amounts, can be an insidious killer. Green campaigners have fought to reduce pollution in rivers and cut the use of pesticides in the countryside, which has killed millions of birds and mammals such as otters and foxes. They have also succeeded in persuading governments to reduce the invisible air pollution that causes acid rain, killing fish in thousands of lakes and decimating the forests of north and central Europe.

Perhaps the biggest task is to preserve intact the habitats for the world's wildlife from farmers, mining companies and the constant spread of towns and cities. In the past five years groups such as Friends of the Earth have raised our level of awareness of environments such as the rainforests. People have woken up to the extraordinary biological diversity of our planet, much of it contained within the rainforests. It is all very well to fight for the elephant, or tiger or panda, but these are single species among millions. Only by preserving the habitats themselves can we hope to protect them all.

Many of the environmental groups spent 1991 preparing their evidence and addressing their lobbying towards the Earth

Summit, to take place in Brazil in June 1992. The summit is a major United Nations conference, just 20 years after the Stockholm Conference, which first alerted the world to the state of the global environment.

Governments and the United Nations will be pressed to sign a 'biodiversity treaty' — an umbrella declaration intended to preserve the world's wildlife in all forms. In addition, politicians attending the summit may also be asked to sign a global climate treaty aimed at reducing the greenhouse effect, by which air pollution is thought to be warming our planet. The unprecedented nature of the predicted change to climate and sea level would pose a direct threat to the planet's biodiversity. There will be discussions, too, about ways to halt the spread of the world's deserts, to control pollution of the oceans and to prevent destruction of the rainforests.

But as international agencies increasingly adopt the ideas of environmentalists, the green groups are beginning to think more radically about how the world's wild lands can best be preserved. In the rainforests, for instance, they have found common cause with groups like Survival International in preserving the way of life of the tribal groups of the forests.

The environmentalists' thinking is that, since these people have successfully lived in the forests for thousands of years, using the plants and animals to provide them with food and medicines, they should be left in charge of the forests. The rest of the world should attempt to learn from them — about their sophisticated farming methods or their knowledge of the medicinal qualities of plants. Only by preserving the way of life of these people, who live in harmony with their environment, can the world hope to preserve its wild lands.

Fred Pearce

Below: Pollution is perhaps even more of a burning issue than wildlife conservation in attempts to ensure the survival of our planet. Friends of the Earth have led the way in pressurizing governments to control acid rain and other forms of invisible air pollution.

ACTION IN CONSERVATION

Right: The bottle bank is among the more obvious signs of a new conservation-conscious generation. Ten years ago they barely existed, but now no self-respecting local council can afford to be seen without one.

Below: Campaigning on behalf of threatened species is not necessarily a new phenomenon. This RSPB-inspired protest took place in London's West End and was aimed at those fashion-conscious women who wore feathers in their hats. It took place in 1911.

Threats to species, global warming, acid rain and our other environmental problems appear huge and daunting. Governments, which have the power to take action in these matters, too often appear hesitant or unconcerned. Politicians always have to look to their chances in the next election, and are aware that powerful groups may have vested interests in opposing environmental change. As a result, immediate issues such as pit bull terriers and dog licensing tend to take priority over fundamental but long-term questions including the environment.

Still, great advances in environmental protection have been brought about by the actions of concerned citizens, particularly when they have worked in concert through pressure groups. Sometimes these groups operate by providing the public with information and motivating them to act. This method bypasses politicians altogether.

The alternative method is to focus public attention on an issue which can be put right

only by political action. A good example is the trade in endangered species, highlighted by (among others) the World Wide Fund for Nature (WWF). Growing public interest turns the issue into a matter of short-term concern and soon politicians are competing with each other to claim a passionate interest in small monkeys and rhinoceroses' horns.

Extensive media attention is needed for both these methods and, generally speaking, the most celebrated pressure groups have been the ones prepared to undertake direct action, in the form of brave stunts performed on behalf of the environment. Greenpeace is the outstanding example here. But few of Greenpeace's 400,000 UK supporters will ever be directly involved in carrying out these actions themselves, or would ever want to, however much they may admire them.

Friends of the Earth (FOE), although often spoken of in the same breath as Greenpeace, works in a rather different way — a way designed to involve large numbers of its supporters. Its London-based campaigners arrange highly successful stunts: in 1991 huge bottles descended on Parliament to publicize the fact that so few

glass bottles carry a deposit. Their slogan was 'Bring back the bring-back'. But these actions are backed up by a network of over 300 local groups in England, Wales and Northern Ireland. For this campaign, for example, the local groups had surveyed public opinion in their areas in order to demonstrate to businesses and politicians that people would accept and even welcome returnable bottles.

Other groups succeed, rather more quietly, by getting their supporters involved in the action *en masse*. The British Trust for Conservation Volunteers (BTCV) involves about 55,000 young — and not so young — people every year in practical conservation projects such as planting trees, managing woodlands and wetlands, and protecting badger setts from diggers. Equally active is the Council for the Protection of Rural England (CPRE) which, together with associated groups in the other countries of the UK, has a network of local groups and some 40,000 supporters. The supporters participate in its work of monitoring and protesting about unsympathetic developments, whether a consequence of town planning or due to road schemes.

The alternative strategies adopted by various voluntary groups are, to a large extent, complementary. They offer members of the public a wide choice, so that they can join a radical or a relatively 'establishment' group and find an organization that will

Overleaf: Belize is a major area of international conservation action. The survival of tropical rainforests is of fundamental importance to every nation, and a programme to save the forests in Belize has been established by the people themselves, working in conjunction with groups and organizations from several other countries.

Below: A dolphinarium was a feature of almost every zoo or adventure park until just a few years ago. The popular reaction against such entertainment has since been such that few now remain. This protest is outside Ocean World in Florida.

Above: The state of the ozone layer was once the preserve of a few specialized scientists, but it became a source of dinner-table conversation thanks to the campaigning work of Friends of the Earth. Consumer pressure has subsequently ensured that many manufacturers have had to remove all ozone-destroying chemicals from their aerosols.

less favourable. With many of its members coming from a diving or biological background, the MCS has a great deal of expertise and its advice is therefore welcomed by official conservation bodies and by parliamentary committees. But the success with which Greenpeace has allied itself in the public mind with the protection of the seas means that the MCS finds itself having to compete for potential members with a much more powerful rival.

A further difficulty is that, with the growing number of environmental groups and their increased commitment to campaigning, there is an inevitable danger that campaigns will overlap. Plantlife, the Royal Society for Nature Conservation (RSNC), FOE and a number of other groups, many of them small and specialized, are all interested in publicizing the need to conserve Britain's remaining peat bogs. In this instance they formed a campaign partnership, bringing together some of the movement's largest organizations and some of its minnows such as the British Dragonfly Society. Similarly, this year a consortium of groups launched a campaign to protect and promote Britain's hedgerows, a home to plants, birds and wild mammals.

Competition is not always so easily overcome. Ironically, on other occasions the same factors can lead to issues being neglected, since in choosing their campaigns groups need to balance the importance of the issues against their likely public appeal. All groups will steer away from a campaign issue which is seen as unexciting or 'unsexy'.

benefit from the kind of support that they wish to give.

But this complementarity does not mean that all groups have an equal chance to grow. In particular, media interest and a high public profile bring success not only in campaigning terms; they also act as a form of advertisement for new membership. Not surprisingly, this has meant that two comparatively young groups, FOE and Greenpeace, have risen quickly to take their place among the three or four best-known and largest environmental organizations in the world, with well over half a million supporters between them.

Their success is looked on enviously in other parts of the movement and other groups have tried to learn from it. Other organizations are also finding that it makes sense to devote more of their energies to campaigning than they used to. In this way some of the strategic differences between the groups are diminishing.

The large organizations have budgets and the publicity that makes further growth reasonably likely. Small groups, such as the Marine Conservation Society (MCS), with around 5000 supporters, find the situation

This problem should not be exaggerated. A group such as FOE can make even an esoteric issue such as the energy efficiency of domestic appliances (how well insulated your fridge or oven is) into a matter of public concern. Still, as a general rule many groups would be eager to campaign on behalf of the badger or of threatened whales; endangered earwigs would find fewer champions.

Campaigning is a very effective form of action for conservation. For example, a nature conservation group that wants to protect an endangered habitat faces a choice: it can either try to acquire examples of the habitat itself or aim to get the government and local authorities to include that habitat in their nature reserves. The first method gives the group a lot of control but places huge demands on it. It will need to raise a lot of money to get the lease and is then faced with a continuing duty to manage the land. If, on the other hand, it changes the government's mind about the value of the habitat, the government will pay the costs, it should look after the site, and it can certainly afford to protect larger areas than a voluntary group can. So campaigning is cost-effective. Recognizing this fact, both the Royal Society for the Protection of Birds (RSPB) and the RSNC, Britain's leading nature conservation organizations, are devoting more of their funds and energies to campaigning.

Exactly the same logic applies in the case of the rainforests. It may be possible for conservationists to buy small plots of forest as a kind of showpiece, but only governments or huge corporations can safeguard tens of thousands of square kilometres. And when you turn to the atmosphere it becomes obvious that the only way to combat global warming or to limit damage to the ozone layer is through campaigning.

It is easy to point to examples of successful campaigns. In Britain, FOE virtually single-handedly saw to it that ozone-destroying chemicals were removed from aerosols. Greenpeace has recently led a consortium of groups and a few friendly governments in a campaign to halt mineral exploitation in Antarctica and to make it a wilderness continent. At the other end of the scale, in 1987 small groups of local people in England successfully opposed plans by the government's nuclear waste company, Nirex, to dump large quantities of nuclear waste underground in rural areas. And nature conservation groups in Northern Ireland last year managed to overturn plans for a major harbour development in Belfast which would have destroyed some valuable bird breeding-sites.

But, as the diversity of these examples shows, there is no simple recipe for success

Below: The British Trust for Conservation Volunteers is a leading exponent in the art of getting the public directly involved in practical schemes, such as the clearing of overgrown rivers. Many unofficial groups have since followed their example.

in campaigning. Some campaigns, such as the promotion of ozone-friendly aerosols, have to be targeted at members of the public. Others, for example the RSNC campaign to get the British government to strengthen the protection for designated wildlife sites, have to be aimed at the authorities. Perhaps inspired by the environmentalists' campaign successes, their opponents are now striking back. For example, the British nuclear industry frequently advertises in the newspapers, telling readers about the possible benefits of nuclear power. It has also invested heavily in an interpretation centre at Sellafield. By and large, industry's budgets for public relations far exceed the amounts campaign groups are able to spend.

Lastly, to an increasing extent, campaigners need to work at even higher levels, with the European Community on European issues, or with the United Nations on global ones. Time and again — over water quality, over bathing beaches, over dumping in the North Sea — it has been necessary to show that other European countries have higher environmental standards than we do. Such an international approach is time-consuming and places a heavy burden on campaign groups' resources, but it has produced a good record of successes.

In this decade, campaigning will be recognized as the leading skill of environmental groups. Already their professionalism is acknowledged by other lobbyists: in 1989 FOE was voted Pressure Group of the Year by the magazine of the advertising and marketing industry, *Campaign*.

To campaign successfully, groups need members and funds. They may nevertheless take different lines on the kinds of sponsorship and gifts they are willing to accept. Oil companies, aware of the bad press they receive from oil spills and air pollution, are keen to be associated with environmental groups. And BTCV, for example, receives sponsorship from Esso and Shell. FOE and Greenpeace would not accept such support. No matter how much the organizations are in agreement about the value of conservation, there will always be a degree of competition between them. Just as in the marketplace, competition can often be a very good thing. It forces campaign groups to be innovative in their stunts: each is competing to make itself more newsworthy than the others and to reach politicians in new ways. It also leads groups to pioneer methods for raising money. The RSPB offers a Visa card with a proportion of all you spend going to the society; the RSNC has responded with a Mastercard. But competition can be wasteful, as the danger of duplication proves.

Just as vicars are supposed to lead lives free of sin, green groups need to avoid causing environmental damage. If they fail to live up to the green standards they advocate, they leave themselves open to accusations of hypocrisy. We would expect all environmental organizations to use recycled paper and low-energy lighting. But in other areas it is less easy to define environmental 'sins'. All groups need to distribute far more membership forms and requests for donations than are actually used; so does this mean they are adding to the problem of waste? In short, how can green ends be balanced against less-than-green means?

Other issues are also neither cut nor dried. FOE receives sponsorship from an (environmentally friendly) cosmetics

Right: Several banks and building societies have found a lucrative way of wooing new custom, by making a small donation from the profits of their credit cards to well-known wildlife organizations.

company, something very radical Greens would reject on the grounds that cosmetics are unnecessary and a waste of resources. Worse, the complex nature of international finance means that it is hard for any group to avoid unwitting use of tainted money through banks and investments.

WWF was last year criticized for its investment policy. WWF receives many large donations, some of which it invests long-term to secure a regular income for its work. Clearly it needs to make such investments as shrewdly as possible, but to WWF's embarrassment critics revealed that some of the companies supported by its investment fund had interests in either nuclear power or uranium mining.

No group can really evade these problems. They all need bank accounts but cannot control what banks do with their deposits. When Greenpeace looked for an ethical bank it could not find one, so all it can do is limit its investments. It would seem, in fact, that it is just as hard to be fully green as it is to be wholly good.

Innovation and continued vitality are nevertheless the challenges of the 1990s for campaign groups. By now, many of the most straightforward campaigns have already been run and won. The FOE campaign against ozone-eating aerosols was a classic of its kind. The issue could readily be explained to consumers — they knew which products to avoid, there were already alternatives available and the consumer suffered no hardship as a result. Few cases are likely to offer such a perfect campaign target in the future. Pressure groups will need great imagination and innovative thinking if they are to continue their successes as the issues become more complex, particularly if economic circumstances incline consumers to put price before environmental friendliness.

Steven Yearley

THE HUMAN DIMENSION

Not many people have heard of the Pribilof Islands, and fewer still know much about them. These remote, windswept islands in the Bering Sea between Alaska and the USSR are hardly visited by outsiders, except for small numbers of tourists who arrive by plane in the brief Arctic summer. They go there in July to see spectacular multi-species seabird colonies and brilliant displays of wild flowers. But probably the main reason they go is to marvel at the colossal concentrations of northern fur seals hauled up on their breeding beaches. Nowhere else in the far north, and in only a handful of other places in the world, is it possible to see so many mammals gathered together in one place.

It sounds like paradise — but, tragically, for the native inhabitants of these isolated islands it is turning into paradise lost. The local people, who are called Aleuts, are literally losing their will to live. In the 12 months up to June 1991, 24 suicides and 80 attempted suicides were reported among a population of just 600 on the main island of St Paul. In addition, there were 17 alcohol-related deaths in the first half of 1991.

The reason for this tragedy appears to be a fierce attack on the Aleuts and their way of life, first by environmental groups headed by Greenpeace, and latterly by American animal rights activists. In past centuries, the northern fur seals were slaughtered on a massive scale for their skins. But numbers declined until in 1957 the USA, Canada, Japan and the Soviet Union agreed to manage the harvest on a sustainable basis. As recently as the mid-1970s, some 50,000 young male fur seals were clubbed to death each year out of the Pribilof population of 1.5 million.

Commercial sealing was banned altogether in the early 1980s. But the Aleuts in the Pribilofs were allowed an annual quota of 1000 animals, strictly for food and to provide a link with their traditional culture. The harvest is closely monitored by US government officials, who also ensure that all the skins are buried so that they cannot be sold. Nevertheless, the animal welfare groups have kept up the pressure.

'I don't give a hoot what it means to be an Aleut,' Patricia Feral, president of Friends of Animals, told *The European* newspaper. 'They talk about the death of their culture. What culture? They just drink, smoke marijuana, hit children, shoot puffins, and clobber seals on the head.'

Larry Merculieff, a spokesman for the Aleuts, agrees that there are desperate social problems, but says the activists have got things back to front. He maintains that the problems actually stem from the Aleuts being pressured to abandon their traditional lifestyle. 'There are only 3000 Aleuts in the world, and we are the largest community. But our cultural fabric is being destroyed. Suicide was practically unknown here, yet now we have an epidemic.'

Above: Life has lost much of its meaning for the Inuits of Greenland and northern Canada following the collapse of the international market for seal skins. Without the income from the sale of pelts, it is hardly worth their while going hunting.

Merculieff also believes that, by focusing on the fur seal harvest, the animal rights groups are obscuring a much more important issue. There is a growing environmental crisis in the Bering Sea which is virtually ignored. Seven million seabirds may have died since 1976, and the fur seal population is declining despite the ban on hunting.

The plight of the Aleuts highlights a problem that can be seen in many forms in different parts of the world, and is likely to become more widespread as human numbers continue their upward spiral and the remaining wild animals come under ever greater pressure. Less dramatic but equally poignant examples can be seen elsewhere in the north. One only has to visit the Inuit (Eskimo) communities of northern Canada to observe the end result of the pan-European seal-skin ban, enacted, with much rejoicing, in 1983. The original focus of the campaign was the harvest of 'white-coats' or harp seal pups farther south off Newfoundland and in the Gulf of St Lawrence. But it resulted in a collapse of

the market for all seal skins. The Inuits of the north once hunted adult ringed seals, for instance. They made good use of the meat, blubber and skins, and in recent times the sale of some surplus skins allowed them to buy necessities they could not obtain from nature, such as fuel for their boats. Now it is hardly worth while to go hunting, so whole communities are on the dole. Listless and dispirited, the young men have little to do except hang around the settlements, spraying the walls of their houses with graffiti and waiting for the next shipment of kung fu videos.

Norway is a country where fishing, including catching seals and whales, is not just traditional but inseparable from the national culture. And many Norwegians are angry that they are being prevented from whaling by what they consider an emotional and unfair campaign. 'It is militant environmentalists who have ruined me,' says whaler Steinar Bastesen, who has had to sell his boat. 'Fishing is the only thing I know, and I mean to keep on doing it.'

Unfair? Scientists, except those from Norway, Iceland and Japan, do not believe that commercial whale stocks can sustain a revival of whaling. There is also an emotional dimension — as with seals — since catching whales, even with the modern explosive harpoon, is undoubtedly painful and shockingly inhumane.

Nearer home, in the Faeroe Islands north of Shetland, there is an annual round-up of pilot whales. In former days, the islanders depended on this meat for food, but nowadays they are a wealthy community (from fishing) and the catch is continued mainly for the sake of tradition. The small whales are herded into a bay where they are caught with steel hooks, dragged on to the beach, and have their throats cut. It is definitely traumatic for the animals, and unpleasant to watch. The Whale and Dolphin Conservation Society reckons that nowadays the catch is enjoyed more for the sport involved than for any deep cultural fulfilment, and opposes it on humanitarian grounds. Conservation is not an issue: only 1000 animals are caught, and this level is almost certainly sustainable.

But as with the fur seals of the Pribilofs, humanitarian concerns are in danger of-overshadowing a deeper problem: the

mounting level of pollution in the North Atlantic. Indeed, analyses of pilot whale carcases show that the level of some substances, such as PCBs, would render the meat unfit for human consumption in Britain.

Sometimes animals are protected solely for the purest of conservation motives: where they would become extinct unless protected. Tiger conservation has been very successful in India, but people living near tiger reserves have to suffer attacks on their domestic animals, and sometimes on their friends and

Above: Huskies have always been identified with hunting in, and the exploration of, the polar regions. The increased use of motor transport, and moves to ban the dogs because of their potential to bring disease to such places, means that many packs now face the prospect of being put down.

Left: Whalers blame emotional and unfair campaigns by militant environmentalists for destroying their traditional livelihood. They believe that the social and commercial implications of international whaling bans are not being given due weight in the argument.

families. It is often hard to reconcile the needs of conservation, let alone the western humanitarian ethic, with the needs of the human beings most directly affected. You can pay compensation for a dead cow, but money does not bring back a child.

Complicated though the issues are, what is not in question is that 'people power' gets results. The great anti-fur wars of the 1970s and 1980s, for example, effectively knocked the bottom out of the fur trade. These efforts started as a conservationist campaign directed mainly against the exploitation of the large cats. Actors and writers like Elizabeth Taylor, Mia Farrow, Nanette Newman, Iris Murdoch, Brigid Brophy, Maureen Duffy and Margaret Drabble were all prepared to pledge never again to wear the skin, fur or feathers of any wild animal.

But very quickly conservationist concerns became indistinguishable from humanitarian ideals. Soon, all fur coats became unacceptable, whether made from the pelts of wild animals or those bred for

the purpose, such as mink and fox. The European ban on the import of seal-skin products would never have been achieved without massive petitions and avalanches of letters calling on politicians to do something. The International Fund for Animal Welfare was the main mover and shaker in this particular campaign. The outcome showed clearly that when enough people want change, and make their feelings known, politicians are forced to take action. Similarly, the recent campaign by the World Wide Fund for Nature (WWF) and Greenpeace to change the British government's attitude towards mining in Antarctica depended on conveying the wishes of the people, in the form of letters to MPs and signatures on petitions.

There has been great success in dealing with the enormous dolphin mortality resulting from tuna fishing, especially with the use of drift nets. Earth Island Institute in the USA instigated a boycott against the firm of H J Heinz, which owns StarKist, the world's

Below: 'Leopard skins look better on leopards', claims the conservationist campaign. So many people now agree that the fur trade can surely never be the same again.

largest canner of tuna. It was not long before Heinz announced it would use only tuna caught by 'dolphin-friendly' methods. Two other leading American tuna canners quickly followed suit. In the UK, the Whale and Dolphin Conservation Society negotiated with the tuna industry to achieve similar ends. A public boycott was not necessary here (the industry was well aware of what had happened across the Atlantic), and to date three-quarters of the trade has signed an undertaking promising to comply with the requirements. This includes leading brands such as Princes and John West, and major supermarket chains like Asda, Co-op and Safeway. Promises are important, but both in the USA and the UK, verification of what is actually going on remains a problem.

When WWF wanted to persuade Thailand to enforce stricter compliance with trade bans on certain animals, and to clamp down on Bangkok's notorious animal markets, it found that the mere threat of calling for a tourist boycott was enough to galvanize the Thai authorities into taking action.

People power provides vital help for the International Primate Protection League (IPPL) in its campaign against the use of young chimpanzees by Spanish beach photographers. IPPL relies on tourists visiting the costas, and also the Balearic and Canary Islands, to report cases of this shocking — and illegal — use of chimps. Despite their efforts, there may still be as many as 100 chimpanzees in use at Spanish resorts. It is a profitable business for the photographers, who can make up to £800 per day, and at a local level the Spanish authorities need more persuasion that this is actually an abuse, not a legitimate use, of wildlife.

On a more general level, people are increasingly aware of the importance of seeking out environmentally friendly products, and changing to a less wasteful lifestyle. There is a long way to go, but

countries like Britain are gradually becoming more environmentally conscious. Taking their lead from the environmental organizations, more and more individuals are demanding that industry and government clean up their act.

Nevertheless, the path is seldom easy, and especially where people from rich, developed countries seek to persuade those in poorer countries to share their views. A principal difficulty lies in distinguishing between purely environmental and conservation concerns, and those based on humanitarian or animal rights issues. If an animal is in danger of extinction, the situation is relatively easy to explain, though not necessarily to solve.

But when humane treatment of animals is at stake, the situation is trickier and demands great understanding and tact on the part of those promoting change. Aggressive and insensitive campaigning, like that directed at the Pribilof islanders by the Friends of Animals, is no more morally respectable than the fierce proselytizing of old-time missionaries.

Nigel Sitwell

Above: Whether at the hands of the organ-grinder or the Spanish beach photographer, the exploitation of young primates has always been a profitable business. Many environmental organizations are still calling for greater legislation to stamp out completely a practice that is already illegal in many places.

WILDLIFE ORGANIZATIONS

Above: More than 20 plant species have vanished altogether from their natural habitats in Britain and Ireland this century. Thanks to Plantlife, these marsh marigolds narrowly avoided becoming another of them.

Below: The bloody cranesbill is interesting because botanists have discovered a gradual decrease in the width of its leaf lobes from west to east Europe. The Royal Society for Nature Conservation is working to ensure that its wild meadow habitat survives.

With the growing awareness of species extinctions and other environmental problems, hundreds of voluntary groups around the world are striving to protect endangered animals and plants and their habitats. Governments, too, have committed themselves to species protection through both national action and international measures. The problem of species loss is too big for a single group to tackle in isolation and the trend of species extinctions will be slowed down only through cooperative efforts at local, national and global levels.

Three of Britain's leading conservation organizations are the World Wide Fund for Nature (WWF) UK, the Royal Society for Nature Conservation (RSNC) and the Royal Society for the Protection of Birds (RSPB). They operate in different ways and have different priorities but all exert a considerable influence on the fate of wildlife at home and abroad. Governments may hold the power and resources to take decisive conservation action, but they are usually slow to act and need to be pressured by public opinion.

The organization best known for the conservation of endangered species is WWF. The UK branch of WWF was established in 1961. In the early days the organization concentrated on raising money to protect large mammals such as the rhinoceros, elephant and, of course, the giant panda, WWF's symbol. WWF's concerns have diversified considerably over the past 30 years, with an increasing emphasis on habitat conservation and sustainable utilization of the earth's resources. But species conservation remains an important part of WWF-UK's work.

More emphasis is now being given by WWF-UK to the protection of plants and invertebrates, which have often been neglected in the past. In Britain over 300 plant species are threatened with extinction, and 20 have disappeared over the past 100 years. WWF-UK has recently funded research into the best way to protect the early spider orchid which is found at only a few locations in southern England. Ploughing and disturbances continue to threaten these remaining sites. WWF-UK also funds

projects carried out by Plantlife, a new organization launched in 1990 to save plants and campaign for plant conservation.

WWF-UK regularly works with over 100 voluntary organizations and individuals to provide financial assistance for conservation projects, research and campaign issues. About 20 per cent of the conservation projects funded by WWF-UK are carried out by the Wildlife Trusts. There are 48 Wildlife Trusts, which promote nature conservation primarily through acquisition and management of important wildlife habitats, carrying out ecological survey work, publicizing local conservation needs and involvement in local planning issues. The national coordinating body for the Trusts is RSNC, which also oversees 50 Urban Wildlife Groups.

RSNC has a total membership of over 250,000. It manages nearly 2000 nature reserves covering over 560sq km. RSNC also campaigns on important national conservation issues. On Midsummer's Day

Below: The Burren, an outstandingly beautiful area in western Ireland, is under threat from development. Plantlife — an organization established in 1990 to save rare plants and to conserve the environment in which they live — has joined local people to protect it.

Right: This is Minsmere, a reserve in Suffolk owned by the Royal Society for the Protection of Birds. Although primarily concerned with bird conservation, the society owns land that is vital for the survival of many wild flowers.

Below: A recent habitats directive issued by the European Commission may prove to be the last chance to save many endangered plants and animals, such as the European lynx.

1991, the Society launched a campaign to save Britain's wild-flower meadows.

In Britain, birds remain the most popular form of wildlife and RSPB continues to be one of the country's conservation leaders, with a membership of over 865,000. The work of the Society includes research, education, lobbying and campaigning, as well as the creation and management of nature reserves. RSPB has a network of 119 reserves covering a total of 761sq km of the British countryside.

The role of the voluntary conservation organizations in the UK is increasingly important at present, in the face of the reorganization of the government's own agency for conservation. With the dismantling of the Nature Conservancy Council (NCC) in early 1991 into separate offices for England, Scotland and Wales, there are very real concerns that some of the conservation gains of the past ten years will be rapidly reversed. Of particular concern is the future of internationally important sites in Scotland, such as the Flow Country and the Cairngorms. RSPB and other voluntary organizations have campaigned throughout the 1980s for the protection of these sites. Now the interests of large landowners in Scotland are

likely to carry more weight than the concerns of conservation organizations.

As well as helping to protect the best wildlife habitats within the countryside, the voluntary conservation organizations are increasingly involved in protecting urban wildlife and enhancing green spaces within Britain's towns and cities. For many people, seeing wild plants and animals in their local parks or areas of wasteland provides their only chance to see wildlife at first hand and to become involved in conservation. About three-quarters of all people in England and Wales never visit the countryside or only go there a few times a year for the odd day out. The work of RSNC's 50 Urban Wildlife Groups and other organizations involved in greening our towns and cities has developed rapidly over the past ten years, so that the 1980s have proved to be the decade of urban conservation.

The London Wildlife Trust, which, like the other Wildlife Trusts, is affiliated to RSNC, was set up in 1981 to protect important wildlife sites in London. It now looks after 60 habitats, including meadows, wetlands and woodlands, and is campaigning to protect many more sites. Among the sites protected by the Trust is Camley Street Natural Park, a haven for wildlife bounded by the Regent's Canal and the busy streets and railways of King's Cross and St Pancras. Camley Street Natural Park includes a large pond, meadows and woodland created out of land which had been used as an unofficial

rubbish tip. A wildlife garden has been created, to demonstrate what city gardeners can do to improve the environment and attract wild creatures, and the site has played an important part in helping children learn about wildlife. Eight years of enthusiasm and hard work, much of it voluntary, have created the Camley Street Park, but its future is far from secure. The London Wildlife Trust is fighting plans for the Channel Tunnel railway terminal at King's Cross which would destroy the Park and its facilities. The fate of Camley Street rests with Parliament, and a decision on legislation concerning the future of the King's Cross area is expected in 1992.

As well as protecting sites and species of local and national importance, British voluntary conservation groups also have a major role to play in international conservation affairs. Increasingly, conservation policy in the UK is directed by the European Commission and European Parliament. RSPB, WWF-UK and RSNC are all involved in lobbying for effective European conservation measures. The policies of the European Community (EC), particularly through the Common Agricultural Policy (CAP), which provides subsidies for food production, have been responsible for dramatic changes in the countryside throughout Europe. Conservation organizations are now calling for basic reform of the EC's support for agriculture as part of the greening of the EC as Europe moves closer to political and economic unity.

European legislation to protect bird species was introduced ten years ago in response to concern about the annual slaughter of migratory birds in southern Europe. Conservation groups are now campaigning for the introduction of legislation to protect other groups of animals and plants and also habitats such as wetlands and traditional meadows which are under threat throughout Europe. A habitats directive has already been drafted by the European Commission. Its introduction may

provide the last chance to save at least some of the 1500 flowering plant species which are threatened with extinction within the EC, together with endangered animals such as the European lynx, brown bear, otter, black vulture and many species of butterfly.

Further afield, UK-based voluntary conservation organizations are supporting conservation around the world, either directly through funding their own projects or by supporting local conservation groups. Most countries now have a voluntary conservation movement, but often in tropical countries membership is low and finance is limited. Also, freedom of speech on environmental issues is not always guaranteed.

Most organizations now realize that conservation measures must involve local people and take their needs into account. Failures in the past have usually resulted from conservation projects being designed without consulting the local people whose livelihood depends on the wise use of natural resources. This has been particularly the case in the development of national parks. Legally designated national parks and other protected areas are essential for habitat and species conservation. At present only around 4 per cent of the species-rich tropical rainforests are protected and so voluntary conservation groups are working

Above: As well as many species of wild flowers, the future of many butterflies, like this inappropriately named common blue, is threatened by Britain's vanishing meadow sites.

Right: Three rare west African antelopes, including this bongo, live in the Gola Reserve in Sierra Leone. The area has now become a focus of RSPB's international conservation initiatives.

with governments and inter-governmental agencies to expand protected area coverage. WWF is campaigning to increase the amount of protected rainforest to 10 per cent of the total area by the year 2000.

As one of its major activities in tropical forest conservation WWF-UK is helping to fund the Korup National Park in Cameroon. The Park protects the most species-rich area of tropical rainforest in Africa, the habitat for over 250 species of birds, a quarter of all African monkey species and a remarkable diversity of plants. Korup National Park was established by law in 1986, but legislation alone will not ensure that the rainforest and its species remain undisturbed. Active management of the Park is required, including measures to prevent poaching and illegal forest clearance. To help prevent excessive hunting, WWF-UK is working to create 'support zones' around the Park. In these areas small-scale sustainable hunting, forestry, agriculture and fish-farming are being developed to provide the local people with food and income, while taking pressure off the Park itself. The forests of the Korup area are still not safe from commercial logging pressures, mainly from developed countries, but the National Park project offers the best long-term hope for local people to continue to live in harmony with their natural environment.

The development of local support for conservation is a priority throughout the world. Support for conservation education and local conservation groups overseas is an important aspect of the work of WWF-UK, working with the international headquarters of WWF in Switzerland, national WWF offices in more than 20 other countries and field conservation programmes in well over 100 countries worldwide. WWF-UK is keen to assist local conservation efforts in Britain's remaining overseas dependent territories such as Hong Kong, Gibraltar and the Falklands. Montserrat is a

small island dependency within the Caribbean sometimes described as the 'Emerald Island'. Although only fragments of Montserrat's original rainforest vegetation remain, the island has a rich natural heritage, including the Montserrat oriole, a bird found nowhere else in the world.

The conservation of Montserrat's wildlife and natural habitats is the responsibility of the Montserrat National Trust, a non-governmental organization established in 1970. Since it was first set up, the Trust has received little assistance from the island's government and has struggled financially. The Trust is now supported by a grant from WWF-UK. This is helping to build up its local membership and also to continue developing plans for Montserrat's first National Park. In addition, it enables the Trust to carry out restoration of the island's natural environment, which was devastated by Hurricane Hugo in 1989.

RSPB's international work has focused largely on Europe and on preventing the extinction of birds through excessive levels of international trade. More recently, the Society has become directly involved in conservation of species and habitats in West Africa. In this aspect of its work, RSPB works closely with the International Council for Bird Preservation (ICBP).

RSPB's current rainforest project aims to conserve a patch of forest in Sierra Leone, a West African country which now has only around 4 per cent of forest cover, compared with an estimated original 60 per cent. The site, known as the Gola Reserve, has six of the world's most threatened bird species, together with the rare West African pygmy hippopotamus. The Gola Forest is threatened by forest clearance for the growing of crops, by uncontrolled logging and by hunting. The aim of the Gola Forest Rainforest Programme is to manage the forest both to supply the needs of local people and to ensure its long-term conservation. Areas are being set aside for logging at sustainable levels as well as for strict conservation where no hunting or logging are allowed. The boundaries of these areas are being marked on the ground and trained staff will enforce the regulations.

Voluntary organizations frequently work together in Britain to persuade the government to take action on national or international issues. At an international level there are also strong links between conservation groups strengthened by umbrella organizations such as ICBP and the International Union for the Conservation of Nature (IUCN). ICBP's network of scientists and conservationists helps protect endangered birds all over the world by gathering and publicizing vital information and carrying out priority conservation projects. IUCN is made up of governments, voluntary conservation organizations and individual experts, with nearly 600 members representing 116 countries. All the main British conservation groups are members of IUCN and so can influence its debates and conservation activities.

Protecting the environment is a global responsibility and membership of a conservation organization is a way for everyone to get involved. Until governments become truly green it is up to individuals to keep informed and support organizations that can make a difference.

Sara Oldfield

Above: The International Council for Bird Preservation is based in Cambridge, but is working in conjunction with the Cameroon government on a project in the Kilum Mountains.

Left: The World Wide Fund for Nature has been helping the Cameroon government to fund the creation of the Korup National Park, which is believed to be the most species-rich area of tropical rainforest in the whole of the African continent.

The Communicators
and Educators

We would know next to nothing about so much of the
world's fabulous diversity of creatures were it not for
the work of people who spend their lives working
with wildlife. Researchers, photographers and film-
makers must often work for long periods in the most
arduous and extreme conditions on earth to
discover the secrets of the enthralling creatures that
inhabit the most far-flung corners of the globe.
Similarly the artists and illustrators whose work
illuminates countless wildlife books and
magazines, bringing the words to life.
The articles in this section look less at the animals
themselves than at the people who have made it their
life's work to tell us about them. Here we speak to
some of the great wildlife personalities of our time,
spending time to watch them at their work. The
section also explores the major wildlife institutions
of natural history museums and zoos, revealing a
fascinating behind-the-scenes glimpse into
London's Natural History Museum.

Right: The work of a wildlife film-maker is rarely glamorous and often extremely lonely, uncomfortable, tedious and frustrating. But patience and perseverance will eventually be rewarded with moments of rare beauty and high excitement.

Left: Sir David Attenborough has probably the highest profile of any wildlife film-maker alive. He uses this eminent position to great effect as the figurehead of many vitally important and successful conservation campaigns.

WILDLIFE PERSONALITIES

Above: Sir Peter Scott was one of the founders of the World Wide Fund for Nature in 1961. He also set up the Wildfowl and Wetlands Trust, based at Slimbridge in Gloucestershire.

Natural history programmes first appeared on television in the early 1950s. Public television transmissions had started in 1936, but very few people owned sets in those early days. By 1953, when Elizabeth II was crowned, enough people had TV sets to open living-rooms across the land to family and friends. Millions crowded around the small black-and-white screens — often for the first time — to witness this great state occasion. Suddenly television was no longer an interesting novelty but something everyone wanted. It quickly became the major communications medium and profoundly changed western lifestyles.

That same year, 1953, saw the very first natural history programme on the new medium. It was presented by Peter Scott, founder of the Wildfowl Trust. The series, soon to be named *Look*, was not very sophisticated at first. It relied on Scott's own eloquent charm, combined with his instant drawings and short film-clips, to which he added a live *ad lib* commentary. Peter Scott (who was to be knighted in 1973 for his services to wildlife conservation) had a great deal going for him. He was already well known for his radio broadcasts in *Nature Parliament* (1946–66) and for his books and bird paintings; he was the son of a national hero, Scott of the Antarctic; he was a war hero himself, with two

Right: Armand and Michaela Denis made their first appearance on television in 1954. Their successful *On Safari* programme ran for many years. The Denises were film-makers rather than naturalists, and popularized big game for television.

Distinguished Service Crosses; and he was a naturalist who clearly spoke with great authority. Most important of all, he communicated in a friendly uncondescending way that was guaranteed to appeal to a mass audience.

Look ran from 1953 to 1970 and was a huge success. In his day Peter Scott enjoyed a fame that has probably been equalled only by Sir David Attenborough. In addition to the activities mentioned he made headlines as a champion yachtsman (he won an Olympic bronze in 1936), and as a glider pilot (becoming British national champion in 1963).

Perhaps his greatest role, however, was as a conservationist. He helped found the World Wide Fund for Nature (WWF) in 1961, and undoubtedly its birth would have been much more difficult without his fame and communication skills. Perhaps his masterstroke was choosing to design the WWF's logo in the form of a realistic and cuddly-looking giant panda. 'It has the advantage', he once remarked, 'that you can reproduce it in full colour in black-and-white.' He came up with the idea of keeping Red Data Books to record the threats to endangered species of birds and other animals worldwide, a vital procedure now adopted by conservationists. As a communicator, he had few equals. An American newspaper commented after his unsuccessful America's Cup challenge at the helm of *Sovereign*, in 1964, that he 'never won a race but never lost a press conference'.

Peter Scott ushered in the vogue for natural history on television, and the audience for his programmes created a demand for others. In 1954 Armand and Michaela Denis first appeared on the screen with their long-running series *On Safari*. This was a different kind of programme. Armand was Belgian, and had cut his teeth on documentary films for the cinema. He had spent some time in

Africa, and came to the BBC with a vast amount of animal material. The wildlife sequences concentrated on the large game animals of the east African savannah, intercut with shots of animals that were supposedly Armand and Michaela's pets. The films were very successful, though the formula was somewhat predictable by today's standards. Neither Armand nor his wife were naturalists, however, so their commentaries tended to be rather superficial. And the insular British audience made gentle fun of their undeniably foreign accents (Michaela was British born but made a good job of speaking like her husband).

And then came Sir David Attenborough, whose first *Zoo Quest* programme was shown just three months after Armand and Michaela appeared. He, too, was an instant hit. He is still making natural history films and has achieved star status and a worldwide reputation. Unlike the Denises, and indeed other producers of that era, who used 35mm film, Attenborough chose to break the mould and use 16mm stock. He argued that the larger

size meant extremely heavy and bulky equipment that put severe limitations on the kind of films that could be made. His films, therefore, were very different in a technical sense — and his example was soon followed by others. Wildlife films are now made almost exclusively on 16mm film.

A number of other personalities of those early days should be mentioned. Johnny Morris gained a large and appreciative audience for *Animal Magic*, in which he donned a keeper's uniform and took viewers on an entertaining journey behind the scenes at Bristol Zoo. Joy Adamson and her husband George leapt to fame with *Born Free*, the story of Elsa the lion cub whose mother turned man-eater and had to be shot. Joy's book told of their efforts to raise the cub and return her to the wild. The filmed version of *Born Free* was equally successful, and changed the lives of the stars, Virginia McKenna and husband Bill Travers, who played the Adamsons. They now devote much of their time to animal welfare, in particular the living conditions of zoo animals.

But the Adamsons themselves were somewhat odd people. Joy, for instance, was apt to attend conservationist functions wearing a leopard-skin coat, while George parted from his wife and tended to shun

Left: Johnny Morris was the very popular presenter of *Animal Magic* during the 1960s and early 1970s. He took viewers on visits around Bristol Zoo, showing the background working, and had a distinctive line in putting words into the animals' mouths. Television and audiences are more sophisticated now, and this approach would no longer be appropriate.

Below: George Adamson first came to prominence when he and his wife raised an orphaned lion cub and returned it to the wild. Their story, *Born Free*, was extremely popular as a book and a film.

Right: Gerald Durrell is probably best known for his books, including *My Family and Other Animals* and *Fillets of Plaice*. But much of his most important conservation work goes on in the Channel Islands, at the Jersey Wildlife Preservation Trust.

Below: Jane Goodall has spent the last 30 years carrying out pioneering work with chimpanzees. She has worked tirelessly for the welfare of captive animals as well as campaigning for their conservation in the wild.

people altogether. He continued to care for orphaned lions, however, until his death at the hands of poachers in Kenya in 1990. People like the Adamsons disappeared from view as the public developed more sophisticated tastes in animal books and films.

Gerald Durrell is another figure whose popularity is firmly rooted in the written word, notably in such books as *My Family and Other Animals*. He also captured large audiences with films about his expeditions, but his main work is running his remarkable zoo in Jersey, so he could never spare the time to become a permanent fixture on our screens. He has earned worldwide respect for the solid achievements of his Jersey Wildlife Preservation Trust. His books and television appearances have entertained millions, but he would probably prefer to be remembered for what he has done for endangered wildlife.

A more recent phenomenon is a larger-than-life character called David Bellamy. This craggy, rumpled-looking man with a distinctive voice — part London, part County Durham — is different from most of the other presenters in being a botanist. His success, like David Attenborough's, is based on his enormous enthusiasm for his subject, combined with the authority of his considerable professional scientific knowledge. He does in fact combine his television work with lecturing on botany. Watching Bellamy, the viewer knows that he knows what he is talking about — and at the same time is intrigued and entertained by the force of his unusual personality.

Different again is Jane Goodall, world-famous and highly respected in both academic and popular circles for her pioneering studies of chimpanzees in Gombe National Park, Tanzania. Travelling to Africa with no more qualifications than a secretarial course, she met the great anthropologist Louis Leakey, who encouraged her to study mankind's closest relative. Her life's work, which began in 1960 and still continues, has been described as the longest-running and most significant study of the behaviour of a single animal species ever undertaken. Along the way, she has earned a doctorate in ethology (the study of animal behaviour) from Cambridge University and her work has achieved worldwide renown through numerous television films. Her popular books have entranced readers the world over; *In the Shadow of Man* alone has been translated into 48 languages.

Nowadays, Jane Goodall divides her time between Gombe, travelling the world campaigning for the conservation of wild

chimpanzees, working for the welfare of the many captive animals used for medical research, and raising money for her own research project. She is dedicated to her beloved chimps and her slide-illustrated talks are so fascinating and moving that they invariably end with a standing ovation.

Underwater natural history has been dominated by the Frenchman Jacques Cousteau. For years he and his team of athletic-looking young divers have circled the globe in the yacht *Calypso*, bringing back remarkable films about the wonders of the deep. British television audiences enjoy his films, but in France he is an almost god-like figure, regularly topping lists of the most popular men in the country.

People who command a huge popular following often have their detractors, driven in part perhaps by jealousy, who seek to puncture the myth. Recently, the French magazine *Le Point* ran an anti-Cousteau story accusing him of overpowering self-promotion and a lack of scientific rigour. However, it is widely believed that 'if Cousteau were to run for President of France he would win by a walkover.

In the 1950s and even the 1960s, weeks went by when no natural history or wildlife programmes were shown at all. Now the output is truly amazing. In August 1991, for example, the diligent viewer could have seen some 45 television films and listened to 26 radio programmes dealing with wildlife or the environment. This figure does not include regional variations or *Open University* programmes. And August is not even a popular time of year for this kind of programme.

Besides 'straight' natural history programmes, there are now an increasing number that deal with conservation or environmental issues. Among these, the *Country File* series derives authority from its popular host, John Craven. Another important trend is towards programmes aimed at children,

such as *The Really Wild Show* (*TRWS*). With its fast-paced presentation — mixing graphics, animation, games, quizzes, film-clips, a high-spirited studio audience, and a trio of friendly presenters led by Terry Nutkins — *TRWS* conveys a range of fascinating information about animals that neither children nor their parents could fail to enjoy.

Interestingly, however, the main attraction of *TRWS* lies in the live animals brought into the studio. One recent programme featured two lemurs, a macaw, a squirrel, a rhinoceros beetle, and a tapir. This takes us back to the very earliest TV animal programmes, when George Cansdale brought some of his charges from London Zoo into the Alexandra Palace studio. Some things never change.

Another thing that does not change is that the most popular programmes are those with a well-known and appealing presenter. And because of their fame, these presenters are actively courted by voluntary organizations. People like Attenborough, Bellamy, Durrell, Cousteau, Nutkins and others such as Julian Pettifer and Bill Oddie play a significant hands-on role that goes beyond mere public appearances. This must be good for wildlife conservation and the environment.

Nigel Sitwell

Above: Dian Fossey's work with gorillas was made into an award-winning film, *Gorillas in the Mist*. This, and her books on the subject, have provided among the most compelling of conservation messages.

Opposite: Jacques Cousteau has dominated underwater natural history film-making for many years. His voyages on the yacht *Calypso* have been enjoyed by audiences all over the world, but nowhere more than in his native France, where he is regarded as an almost god-like figure.

An Interview With
Sir David
Attenborough

Right: You know you are in for a visual treat accompanied by a wealth of astonishing information when the youthful figure of David Attenborough appears on the television screen.

There is something reassuring about the sight of the ever-youthful film-maker scrambling up a sand dune, or talking to the camera from the forest floor. You know you are in for a visual treat, combined with a wealth of astonishing information about the natural world. A David Attenborough film is always a voyage of discovery, in the best sense of the phrase, for he is an accomplished storyteller who believes that the pictures you see and the content of the programme are equally important.

Although the viewer is seldom made aware that filming wildlife is anything but easy, the difficulties do show just occasionally. There was one sequence in the *Trials of Life* series, screened in 1991, that showed chimpanzees chasing, and eventually killing and eating, a colobus monkey. For once, David Attenborough was sweating noticeably and seemed out of breath.

He was in the Tai National Park on the Ivory Coast, where the Swiss zoologists Christophe and Hedwige Boesch had been studying chimps for several years. I asked him if it had been as tiring as it looked. 'Yes,' he said, with conviction. 'And the humidity was 100 per cent so you were drenched all day. Actually, it wasn't so hard to follow the chimps as it was to follow Christophe. We

had to leave at first light, before dawn, and go to wherever the animals had been the previous evening. If we were lucky, they were within 20 minutes of the camp ... but on most occasions they were an hour away. And we had to reach them before they moved off, or we might not see them all day. Christophe just started running like a stag, and we had to run too.' David said he managed to keep up all right, but it was tougher for the cameraman, who was more heavily laden.

Filming can be physically demanding, but sometimes it can be dangerous as well.

Above: Filming inside a termite hill was among the more memorable experiences encountered during the making of the *Trials of Life*. These towering mud fortresses can be more than 4m high and are completely enclosed, with no direct entrance.

Above: An early trip to an Indonesian island in search of the world's biggest lizard turned out to be one of David's hairiest adventures. The Komodo dragon is an enormous creature. It can grow to more than 3m long and has been known to overpower and kill water buffalo.

Some of his earliest films, made in the 1950s, involved greater discomfort and danger than more recent ones. During *Zoo Quest for a Dragon* (to find the world's biggest lizard, the Komodo dragon, on Komodo Island in Indonesia), he and colleague Charles Lagus had a narrow escape.

They sailed from Flores to Komodo on a small local boat called a prau. This journey was, and is, extremely hazardous in a small boat, as it entailed navigating fierce tidal races, powerful whirlpools, and half-submerged coral reefs. It turned out that the 'captain' was a small-time gunrunner who had never made the journey before — and had no idea where Komodo was. They survived, but it could have turned out very differently.

Danger of a different kind arose some years later during underwater filming in the Maldives, for one of *The Living Planet* programmes. The team had found a place where a German diver had been feeding sharks, as a kind of tourist attraction. It was arranged that David would sit underwater on a coral outcrop while the cameraman positioned himself off to one side. They decided that David should not himself feed

any fishes to the sharks, since he had not done it before and might not know when to remove his hand.

'So I was sitting there with my arms firmly folded, and these sharks were coming in. And of course they were expecting breakfast. They came closer and closer and then started hitting me on the head as they went past.

'All the time I was thinking the cameraman must be getting some fantastic footage. But I found out later that each time he had been singling out one of the shoal as they approached. And that usually wasn't the one that hit me. So about 90 per cent of the time, while this derring-do was going on and I was being frightfully brave about the whole thing, he never got any of it. I was cheesed off about that.'

He claims it wasn't really all that dangerous as they were 'just reef sharks'. But reef sharks are still sharks, and can grow to 1.5–2m in length.

David Attenborough joined the BBC Talks Department at Alexandra Palace in 1952. He had an abiding passion for natural history and, indeed, a degree in natural sciences, so it is not surprising that he gravitated towards wildlife films. His chance came in 1954 when he persuaded the BBC to embark on the *Zoo Quest* series, based on animal-collecting expeditions for London Zoo. This took him to all parts of the tropics over the next ten years. But at the same time he was producing all manner of other programmes, ranging from political broadcasts to archaeological quizzes, ballet, and gardening and religious programmes.

He left programme-making in 1965 to become Controller of BBC2, changing jobs again in 1969 to become Director of Programmes, with editorial responsibility for both BBC1 and BBC2. However, in 1973 — when many believed he was destined to become Director-General — he cleared out his desk and returned to filming.

After getting his hand in again with a

couple of other series, he wrote and presented the 13-part blockbuster *Life on Earth*. First shown in 1979, it was the most ambitious nature series ever attempted. Its predecessors in style were *Civilisation* and *The Ascent of Man*, both of them definitive and encyclopaedic in scope.

The theme of *Life on Earth* was evolution, but it dealt with the results of evolution, not the mechanisms. 'For example,' Attenborough explained, 'you might look at a frog and say, well, it's a frog, it lives on worms and it breeds in water and so on. But it doesn't necessarily dawn on you that it represents an intermediate stage between the fishes and the reptiles. How does it overcome the disadvantage of having a permeable skin, or solve the problem of breeding away from water? You cannot really understand the nature of a frog unless you understand how it arose and where it stands in evolutionary history. So the idea behind the series was that it should be not just natural history, but a history of nature.'

It proved so successful that it was followed in 1984 by *The Living Planet*, which looked at the earth's environments and how animals and plants adapted to their surroundings. The third part of the trilogy was *Trials of Life*, whose theme was animal behaviour.

'I remember sitting in the bath one day, having finished *The Living Planet*, and thinking that we hadn't done the obvious thing. Why hadn't we done behaviour? Of course, it soon dawned on me that it was too damned difficult!' But he and the BBC Natural History Unit went ahead anyway, though it did prove harder than the earlier series. 'Normally,' explained Attenborough, 'when you are making a natural history programme you get that one hunt sequence, or whatever it is, and then you build up around it. Landscape shots, people getting out of Land Rovers, sunsets. But the difficult bit is that two minutes. And what I was proposing in *Trials* was actually nothing but

that kind of thing. It wasn't enough simply to show an animal sitting there. It had to be copulating, or displaying, or hunting. It had to be doing something.'

Perhaps it was overcoming the difficulties that made the most recent series so exciting for those involved. Attenborough, at any rate, found almost everything about it exciting. For example, in the programme on navigation there was some footage to illustrate how animals have a mental map of their surroundings. 'The elephant shrew has this highly complex circuit of tracks and has such an accurate mental map that it's able to take short cuts. It knows that if it's really in trouble, it can go through country it's never been through before in order to reach a hole. It will go straight across, running like the wind.'

There were many other memorable experiences, 'whether with elephant seals in Patagonia, or Christmas Island crabs, or getting into termite hills. I was horribly spoiled, because we were skimming the cream all the time.' And there are memories from previous series as well. When Dian Fossey took

Below: Close encounters with a shoal of hungry reef sharks, while filming part of *The Living Planet* series, were all in a day's work for the intrepid wildlife programme-maker. David had an eight-year break from filming during which he held a senior executive position with the BBC. But he found that sitting behind a desk somehow lacked the excitement of perching on underwater coral reefs in the Maldives.

Above: 'Being embraced by a mountain gorilla is something you don't forget in a hurry', David recalled after a visit to Dian Fossey in Rwanda.

turn on television to watch a natural history programme. They don't say, "I want to be educated," or, "It's entertainment, I'll get a laugh." They say it's natural history, and it's interesting.'

Like other television personalities, he is often asked to sit on boards and committees. Among his present voluntary activities he is a trustee of the British Museum and of the Royal Botanic Gardens at Kew. He is, naturally, much involved in wildlife conservation. After returning from Rwanda, he helped set up the Mountain Gorilla Project with the Fauna & Flora Preservation Society. 'We raised a lot of money and we are still doing so. We took the view that we had to habituate more gorilla groups for tourists to see, and we had to start an education programme within Rwanda. And it's worked. The fact is that since Dian's death not one gorilla has been lost to poachers, not one. This is very remarkable.'

him to see a family of mountain gorillas in Rwanda, several youngsters spontaneously approached and virtually smothered him in a flurry of hairy black arms.

He also finds intellectual enjoyment in making natural history films. 'There is great pleasure in it because you are finding out new things all the time. The most amazing things. And it's also very enjoyable in a way that writing books and scripts is not, in matching the precise word to the exact frame of film where it has the most impact. You try to make sure it's as accurate as a stiletto, that it's not a vague word, not ambiguous, that it's the one word that really fits in that place.'

I asked David Attenborough if he considered his films to be educational or entertaining. He said he would not categorize them in this way. He believes they are neither — and both. 'I don't pick up a book on natural history and say, "Ah, this is educational." I pick it up because I want to read the thing! And that's why people

David Attenborough has recently become President of the Royal Society for Nature Conservation (RSNC), the umbrella organization for Britain's 47 Wildlife Trusts, 50 Urban Wildlife Groups, and Watch, the educational trust for young people. Despite his concern for conservation in other countries, he says: 'My conscience is clearer about raising money and arguing and agitating about issues in this country.' It is quite easy, he points out, for people to feel good by giving money to help save the Brazilian rainforest. 'But meanwhile, our own woodlands are being bashed down. I feel that people who care about conservation can make real contributions here, and not simply by giving money. They can do something with their local councils, they can help children through a Watch group, they can even help as voluntary nature reserve wardens.'

He plans to travel around the country for the RSNC, visiting local trusts and giving fund-raising lectures and so forth, but he is wary about assuming the role of an expert.

'One thing that embarrasses me continually,' he says, 'is that just because my face is on television, some people consider me to be a sort of guru, a fund of expert knowledge about every aspect of the natural world. And that's not the case. I am not an expert on everything. If I say we should do this or do that, my statements have a kind of authority — a bogus authority — which I am very apprehensive about using.'

Nevertheless, Attenborough does recognize the cumulative effect of films like his own. He believes the success of televized natural history programmes demonstrates that people are not just interested in lions and elephants, or giraffes, but in insects and other animals as well. 'I got into a taxi the other day,' he said, 'and the driver talked very coherently and interestedly about "the selfish gene" and "altruism", and one thing and another.' These are advanced concepts, and Attenborough was impressed. 'It means that people now have a concern, an awareness of the natural

world that has played a part in the whole conservation movement.'

David Attenborough is now 65, though most viewers would find that hard to believe, such is his energy and enthusiasm, and his youthful appearance. He is surely living proof of the principle that doing what you enjoy keeps you young.

He was knighted in 1985, and has been awarded numerous honorary degrees and other awards. But the good news for his millions of fans is that the last thing on his mind is any kind of retirement.

He is already working on a new six-part series about plants. This will not reach our screens for two or three years and he is reluctant to discuss the details, except to say that the subject will be tackled in a new way. Meanwhile, those who care about conserving Britain's wildlife and wild places can see him in person as he travels the country promoting the cause.

Nigel Sitwell

Above: The tent-building bat bites through the central, supporting ribs of large leaves on tropical plants. The two halves then droop downwards and create a shelter under which it can hang, providing protection against wind, rain and strong sunlight. David discovered this one in Costa Rica.

Left: There is little doubt that the film of David Attenborough with the gorillas was an important factor in making people want to travel to Rwanda to see them, which (because of the economic benefit of 'gorilla tourism' to Rwanda) has been the saving of the animals.

NATURAL HISTORY MUSEUMS

Above: This dazzling kaleidoscopic display is part of the permanent Ecology exhibition which opened in March 1991 at the Natural History Museum in London. It explains the basic elements of life and, in this case, of water.

Opposite: London's Natural History Museum houses perhaps the world's best-known and largest collections of wildlife. The construction of this imposing building was begun in 1873 and completed in 1881. Its cathedral-like design was no accident, as the architect Alfred Waterhouse wanted a building worthy of 'housing the great works of the Creator'.

This knowledge is constantly growing through a wealth of research projects, both within natural history museums and outside, but strongly linked with the museum's activities. Perhaps most importantly, museums are in the forefront of education about natural history. The reason behind this was best summed up by the great zoologist, Konrad Lorenz, who said that if you want to control living things, then you must first understand how they work. In other words, looking after wildlife means knowing how it fits into the world's jigsaw. For many people, such an understanding starts in a natural history museum.

London's Natural History Museum is a good example of its kind for several reasons. First, it is one of the world's oldest and largest natural history museums. Second, it has links with institutions and museums worldwide and is involved in many national and international projects to gather, share and apply information. Third, the museum leads the world in natural history education through several means: in addition to its permanent displays of vegetable, animal and mineral matter, the museum continually mounts topical temporary exhibitions, gives talks on natural history and runs field trips.

It all began in the mid-eighteenth century, when a wealthy physician, Sir Hans Sloane, gave his vast natural history collection to the nation. The collection was said to be one of the largest in Europe. In this way, the British Museum was formed in 1753. The first collection was kept at Bloomsbury, but new exhibits poured in over the years as British explorers such as Captain Cook brought back enormous collections of material, and the collection outgrew the available space. By the 1860s, a new site was needed for the natural history exhibits,

Enter London's Natural History Museum (its title since 1989), and one of the first things you will be greeted by is the skeleton of a dinosaur. Walk a small distance beyond it, turn to your left, and your gaze may be met by that of a stuffed tiger. At this point, it would be very easy to ask, 'What has a building full of dead animals, old bones, fossils and pickled plants got to do with wildlife?'

The answer is — a great deal. While the first natural history museums were little more than collections of static specimens laid out to satisfy Victorian curiosity, modern natural history museums have a much wider and more important role. As well as exhibiting things, museums are goldmines of information on an immense variety of subjects in natural history. This information can be used to advantage in such areas as conservation, tropical rainforest management, agriculture, pest control, medicine, law and order, and education.

Above: At the Ecology exhibition you shrink to 8000 times smaller than your normal size and are taken on a tour of the inside of a leaf, to learn about the complex process of photosynthesis.

Below: The Natural History Museum's spectacular Ecology exhibition takes you through the sights and sounds of a tropical rainforest.

that it helped the museum win the title of 'Museum of the Year' in 1980. Another recent modern exhibition looks at a completely different subject — arthropods, a major group of animals without backbones. This group includes insects, a vitally important part of the world's fauna since there are more species of insect than all other species of animal put together. Producing an exhibition which would attract people to look at arthropods was a great challenge, as people tended to be uninterested in such creatures and even to find them repellent. Nevertheless the designers succeeded with an ambitious exhibition that opened in 1988. It was named Creepy Crawlies.

The exhibition is arranged in two sets of displays. The first is a colourful and dynamic display which shows the wide variety of invertebrates, where they live, what they eat and how they spend their time. It shows how invertebrates have adapted to more parts of the world than any other group of creatures. This display includes a mock-up of a typical house, which reveals the range of invertebrates that share our living space and food. The second section of the exhibition looks at each of the major groups of invertebrates and focuses on their amazing adaptations over the past few billion years.

Creepy Crawlies and Human Biology are the first exhibitions at the Natural History Museum in which visitors are able to get involved with natural history. The idea was taken one stage further with a new exhibition that opened in 1990. It was mounted in the basement of the museum and was designed to give children 'hands-on' experience of natural history; suitably, it was called the Discovery Centre. The Centre, which is sponsored by Shell UK Ltd, is a gallery in which children can handle specimens and learn about them through exploration and experiments. Since the new national curriculum for science attaches so much importance to learning through

and a suitable place was found in South Kensington. Construction began on the new British Museum of Natural History in 1873, and it finally opened its doors in 1881.

Although the first displays were obviously limited by resources available at the time, the labels deliberately did not go beyond stating what the species were or where they came from, as visitors were expected to be very knowledgeable about this sort of thing. Since those early days, the displays have changed radically. As well as new materials, advanced methods are used to exhibit specimens. These include moving displays — such as videos and working models of creatures — to entertain and interest visitors of all ages. In addition, the museum started a programme in 1972 to produce a novel form of exhibition. The idea was to put biological subjects in context, not only showing the enormous variety of living things, but also demonstrating how they interact with each other and the environment.

The first of these modern, permanent exhibitions was completed in 1977 and looked at human biology. The design of the exhibition was so unusual and stimulating involvement with the subject, it is particularly useful and topical for school parties.

Exhibitions such as Creepy Crawlies and the Discovery Centre move with the times and are updated as necessary. However, they are also permanent exhibitions designed to form the backbone of the museum. In addition, the Natural History Museum mounts a large number of temporary exhibitions that are often connected with a strong public interest in a subject at a particular time.

The museum hosts talks and field courses that look at varied aspects of the living world, but these activities and exhibitions are only the visible face of the Natural History Museum. There is far more going on behind the scenes in the form of research.

Since its earliest days, the museum has been involved in research. The first investigations simply identified animals and plants and then classified them into groups (taxonomy). The practical applications of taxonomy are immense.

Take medicine, for example. Bilharzia, or schistosomiasis, is a disease that afflicts over 200 million people in all tropical and subtropical regions of the world. It is caused by the larvae of microscopic worms, which develop in the body of an underwater snail. The illness is difficult to treat and can be fatal, but the museum scientists are using special techniques in taxonomy to distinguish the different species of larvae and tropical snails involved, and this knowledge should then help to control the disease.

Perhaps the most exciting application of taxonomy currently is the INBio project in Costa Rica. Working on the principle that in order to conserve a habitat you first need to know what it contains, the aim of the project is to provide information that will help Costa Rica manage and conserve its forests. Museum scientists are training local inhabitants to distinguish the different animals and plants and to produce biological maps of the forest. When the project is finished, Costa Rica's rainforests will be the first in the world to have been examined in this way.

The Natural History Museum is not the only one to be involved in such projects. Local museums are also rich sources of information on local natural history. Many excellent museums all over the world have been modelled on London's Natural History Museum, and can be thought of as moons orbiting it. Their activities and roles are similar, and the staff who run them are, without exception, a dedicated and interested band for whom the richness of nature is more important than other rewards. This dedication and interest is essential, as museums tend to be undervalued and government funding is often inadequate to keep them going — a sad fact, considering how much natural history museums do for wildlife.

Rick Gould

Below: A collection of stuffed animals may no longer be regarded as a terribly appropriate educational aid. But it does provide a unique opportunity to come face to face with creatures from some of the planet's least accessible habitats.

THE YEAR OF THE ZOO

Above: The world's leading zoos strive constantly to raise standards of husbandry, welfare and breeding. They have no choice if they are to continue to be regarded as a legitimate source of conservation, education and entertainment.

Ask zoo directors what zoos are really for and they will say: 'conservation, education, and entertainment'. But this raises a lot of questions. Are zoos really important for conservation — what use is an animal in a cage? Do they serve a purpose in education — especially now that natural history films are so brilliant? As for entertainment, is it really justifiable to keep animals in captivity, simply for our own amusement?

Zoos cannot duck these questions. If zoos really are cruel and unnecessary, then they ought to close. Public opinion matters too, as zoos worldwide derive at least part of their income from visitors. In Britain, visitors provide most or all of the revenue. London Zoo — one of the world's most famous, and Britain's oldest — is now threatening to close, largely because it has only one million visitors per year, and to pay its way needs nearer two million. So what is the truth of the matter?

Many institutions that keep wild animals in captivity have eschewed the title 'zoo'. Some, like Britain's Wildfowl and Wetlands Trust, simply want to move away from the idea of captivity (even though most of their birds are captive). A few of the world's most prestigious and important zoological societies, such as San Diego, USA, and London, have chosen to distinguish between their urban centres (San Diego Zoo, London Zoo) and their country homes (San Diego Wild Animal Park and Whipsnade Wild Animal Park). Other wildlife parks or safari parks grew up in the 1950s and 1960s specifically as a branch of the leisure industry, and as attractions to help pay for the maintenance of crumbling stately homes.

In general, wildlife parks give their animals more room than traditional zoos, and of course animals prefer more room rather than less. But we should not assume that therefore wildlife parks are good, and zoos are bad. Some wildlife and wild animal parks — Whipsnade, San Diego, Cricket St Thomas in Somerset — are involved in serious conservation and, for example, are breeding endangered animals. Others simply keep common species that are easy to breed, so that there are plenty of young for the visitors to look at. When they are young no longer, the zoos dispose of them as best they may. In addition, wide open spaces are not necessarily all that they seem. Giraffes look wonderful on lush English lawns, but the soft, damp grass can play havoc with their hooves — and in open spaces, it can be hard to give them veterinary attention.

The world's serious zoos strive constantly to raise standards of husbandry and welfare, and of breeding. In Britain, the watchdog of standards is the Federation of Zoological Gardens of Great Britain and Ireland, founded in 1966. It was largely responsible for framing the terms of the Zoo Licensing Act of 1981, which seeks to eliminate establishments where standards are deficient. Europe's leading zoos have long cooperated in breeding and other matters, and expect to form their own federation in 1992. Also of significance in promoting standards in zoos is the University Federation for Animal Welfare, based in Hertfordshire.

Another such organization is Zoo Check, founded by the actress Virginia McKenna and her husband Bill Travers, who appeared in the *Born Free* films based on Joy Adamson's books. The organization has appointed itself the task of monitoring conditions in British zoos, and has managed to attain a high profile and to bring to public attention the welfare and psychological health of animals in captivity. However,

Zoo Check is in general 'anti-zoo' and tends to condemn the good and useful zoos along with the not-so-good.

When zoo directors claimed 20 years ago that zoos were for 'conservation', they were treading on fairly thin ice. Although many wild animals were threatened with extinction at that time (though nobody then knew quite how many), very few species were breeding well in zoos, and those that were breeding tended to be the common ones.

Over the last 20 years the picture has changed dramatically. Biologists now estimate that there could be in excess of 50 million different species of animal in the world — about 10 times more than was thought to be the case 20 years ago. It is now believed that about half of all species are in danger of becoming extinct by the middle of the twenty-first century. At first sight, zoos cannot do much against a threat on this scale. There are about 800 reasonably sized and competent zoos in the world, and they could not, with the best will in the world, breed anything like 25 million different kinds of animal.

Above: It is not always easy to persuade some of the larger wild species to reproduce in a zoo environment. This black rhinoceros, born at Chester Zoo in February 1991, is the first to be bred in this country.

Above: Zoological societies are increasingly drawing a distinction between their urban centres and country homes. Whipsnade Wild Animal Park, in rural Bedfordshire, provides space and natural resources for animals which inevitably are not available at the zoo in the heart of London.

Right: A well-run zoo can provide many people with face-to-face contact with rare and exciting animals that they would never otherwise get a chance to see.

Most of the 25 million or so threatened species are insects, chiefly beetles. Zoos might help to save a few insects (for example, London Zoo is breeding iridescent Olympia beetles from Italy) but, generally speaking, the only way to save beetles is in the wild. Mammals, birds, reptiles, and amphibians, however, are a different proposition. There are only about 20,000 species of them in total, of which perhaps half should be considered endangered. The best way to save most of them is simply to try to protect the wild places where they live, but this is more difficult than it may seem, with the rapid destruction of their habitats. Worldwide, wars, poaching and natural hazards also pose serious threats.

The idea that zoos can contribute significantly to conservation by breeding endangered animals is new; the necessary genetic theory has been in place only since the 1970s, and it takes years to establish a serious breeding programme. But about 70 species in Britain and Europe are now subject to such programmes — and most or all of the worthwhile zoos are taking part in them. Chester Zoo, for example, has a particular interest in breeding black rhinoceroses and Asian ele-

phants (which up till now have not bred well in captivity). Bristol Zoo is focusing on Persian leopards, while Marwell Zoo is known for its hoofed animals, such as Przewalski's horse and scimitar-horned oryx. London and Whipsnade, as well as running breeding programmes, have contributed to the science of breeding elephants and rhinos, primates of all kinds, big cats and many birds.

The biggest challenge for conservation is simply that of numbers. Biologists now estimate that if the population of any species in the wild falls much below 2500, then it is liable to become extinct in the next few hundred years as a result of accidents and genetic problems brought about by inbreeding. But to protect 2500 individuals of any large animal would require vast amounts of space.

In practice, zoo populations do not need to be as big as wild populations, because the animals are safer. For example, biologists at the International Rhino Conference in San Diego in May 1991 agreed that 150 of each species of rhino in zoos would provide adequate backup for the wild population. British and Irish zoos now run cooperative breeding schemes, swapping the breeding males around to ensure a good genetic mix for more than 70 endangered species. These are likely to merge with similar schemes on mainland Europe.

The European Community has now announced its intention to close all zoos that are not actively participating in conservation. The legislation is not due for some time, but

we must hope that it will be firmly founded on knowledge of the situation, since there are many ways of being involved in conservation without actually breeding animals. For many species, it is vital to maintain 'bachelor herds', such as exist in the wild — that is, all-male groups that contain the future patriarchs. Such a group, however, may not look like a contribution to conservation. Some zoos also simply provide sanctuary for animals such as injured seals or otters. By no means all of these can breed, or can be returned to the wild, yet the exercise seems worthwhile.

The argument that zoos detract money from conservation endeavours in the wild is for the most part fatuous. Many zoos raise money for such projects — Paignton Zoo is now financing projects to conserve spider monkeys in South America, and London is involved in Africa and the Middle East. More to the point, the total spent on conservation is derisory; the yearly expenditure on all conservation projects in the United States (one of the most generous of countries) would buy only one wing of a Boeing 747. Instead of berating zoos for 'robbing' the wild, we might strive to increase spending on conservation in general, worldwide, by at least one hundred times.

Biologists calculate that about 2000 of the 20,000 land vertebrates are liable to need captive breeding if they are to survive and Dr Michael Brambell, director of Chester Zoo, estimates that zoos between them could manage such schemes for all 2000. Breeding animals for conservation in zoos is not just a matter of producing babies. The relatively small captive populations should contain at least as much genetic variation as the larger wild populations. To ensure that this is the case, breeding in captivity must be managed according to breeding plans which in the US are called SSPs (Species Survival Plans) and in Europe EEP (European Endangered Species Programme). The basic idea of these is to avoid matings between close relatives, and to ensure that all the 'founder' animals in the breeding population have equal opportunity to breed (so that all the genes are passed on from generation to generation). Participating zoos swap animals to ensure these goals are met, and all the animals in the participating zoos are treated as one population.

Careful records of each animal's provenance are preserved in the studbook kept for the species. Dr Peter Olney, based at London Zoo, keeps track of all the world's international studbooks. As he says, the studbooks do not show how to breed

Below: Longleat Safari Park was the world's first drive-through wild animal park. For 25 years the famous prides of lions that live there have been attracting the crowds to the Marquess of Bath's family seat in Wiltshire.

Above: The Asian black bear has been hunted for its fur and its meat for many years. The zoo may provide something of a sanctuary for such creatures.

Below: The survival of the St Lucia parrot is a success story for Gerald Durrell's Wildlife Preservation Trust. More than a fifth of the world population of this vulnerable species are now living and breeding happily at the zoo in Jersey.

animals, but they do provide the data that enables sensible breeding to take place.

There is also, of course, far more to breeding for conservation than the production of cuddly cubs to amuse visitors. If genetic variation is to be maintained, then it is essential to ensure that all (unrelated) mothers in the population have roughly equal numbers of cubs. So if one lioness has five cubs and another has only three, then two from the litter of five should not be used for breeding, as this would unbalance the gene pool of the next generation.

In practice, zoos increasingly control breeding by contraception, so that they produce only a minimum of 'unwanted' animals, but those surplus to requirements do have to be culled. Although this is distasteful, we should perhaps remember that the mortality rate among young animals in the wild is often far higher than among zoo animals (80 per cent of wild lion cubs are liable to die in the first few weeks).

So far, zoos (and other animal breeding centres) can claim to have saved only a few animals from extinction by breeding, but the list is already distinguished. It includes Père David's deer, the European bison, the Hawaiian goose, the Arabian oryx and the golden lion tamarin. All of these have now been returned to the wild, where most of them are doing well. By the middle of the next century, the list of animals saved in zoos could be very long indeed.

What of the second claim, that zoos have a part to play in education? Zoo directors argue that it is largely because zoos inform that they serve the needs of animals. Through zoos, visitors gain direct contact with animals and, in the words of Michael Robinson, director of the National Zoo in Washington, DC, 'go away determined to do something to help them'. It is very difficult to know whether this is true, but for many people, zoos do provide their only opportunity to see exotic animals and, however good the TV films, there is nothing quite like the real thing.

There are many problems and misunderstandings, however, in zoos' attempts to educate. Few have even mastered the art of labelling their animals satisfactorily: labels on enclosures usually give just the creature's name, with a map. Chester is one of the few zoos now employing professional writers to get the information across. Many zoos are turning to other communication techniques: video loops, interactive videos, computer games, working models. There are snags, however. These methods are very expensive and tend to convey only simplified information. The devices themselves can also tend to take over from the message; few people remember what they learn from video games.

The desire to communicate and inform should not disturb the lives of the animals, nor get in the way of attempts to breed them. This potential conflict is not always obvious. There is a strong fashion, particularly in the USA, for presenting animals in 'naturalistic' settings, to show people what their habitats are like. However, confined animals tend rapidly to destroy real trees or coral reefs, so are given fibreglass versions which look wonderful, but are probably meaningless to the animal.

In contrast, an animal may be perfectly happy and breed well in 'unnatural' and even run-down surroundings. Other animals simply prefer to be out of the public gaze. Roan antelope, for example, have tended to do badly in zoos. Richard Kock, director of Whipsnade, guessed the reason: they are woodland animals, and therefore not used to being observed. They look good in their own fields at Whipsnade but are much happier (and healthier) when they are inside their house and out of view. Richard Kock now wants to keep them in woods and allow visitors to watch them only from hides, as if they were wild birds. This would truly combine education with animal welfare.

What of 'entertainment'? A zoo cannot justify its existence simply by entertaining people. There can be no moral justification for old-fashioned menageries, or for circuses. Zoos have to prove that they are good for animals. Yet entertainment is necessary for the conservation message to be put across. Children 'turn off' if they are not entertained when they learn, and people will not go to a zoo, or anywhere else, unless they are given a good time. There is no doubt that zoos do entertain. The statistics and surveys show that people go to zoos for 'a good day out'. But the animals themselves must be allowed to 'entertain' only by living their own lives, in order to arouse the desire to conserve.

Taken all in all, modern zoos have a vast responsibility. The state of the world's wild animals is perilous indeed; and good zoos could make a huge contribution to their salvation. The world's best zoos are meeting their responsibility. But the task is huge and there are many pitfalls and false trails. What zoos perhaps need above all else is what they are trying to create: a well-informed public.

Colin Tudge

JERSEY WILDLIFE PRESERVATION TRUST

Gerald Durrell's Wildlife Preservation Trust at Les Augres, Jersey, established in 1963, is still a model for zoos worldwide. It is founded on the idea that the breeding of animals in captivity can be a valuable aid to the survival of many species, and that wildlife preservation programmes can help catalyse efforts to secure habitat, together with surviving wild populations.

Among Jersey's successes is the programme to save the St Lucia parrot, from the Caribbean. Island animals are especially vulnerable — their populations are generally small to start with and they have nowhere to flee to if their habitat is compromised. This success vindicates the zoo's underlying philosophy. First, the St Lucia parrots at Jersey have thrived. If the St Lucia population is truly threatened they could be multiplied further and used to augment the wild population. The Jersey breeding programme also drew the attention of the St Lucia people to their own parrots. They made the St Lucia parrot their

national bird, and encouraged it in the wild, so that the wild population is now around 300.

Many continental animals also face severe problems, because they can live only in particular environments and die out if those habitats are damaged. The golden lion tamarin of Brazil lives only in the forest bordering the Atlantic, of which a mere 2 per cent now remains. Jersey has been one of the zoos that helped to breed the tamarin. The Brazilians have now established a stronghold for the tamarin in the Una Biological Reserve, and Jersey provided funds to buy a 'corridor' of land to link the two halves of the reserve. It also provided some of the animals that have been returned from zoos since the mid-1980s to restock the reserve. Now, together with other zoos, Jersey is becoming involved in what may prove to be similar projects to save other lion tamarins.

Below: By breeding just a few endangered species, like these snow leopards, the work of Jersey zoo is designed to help them survive in the wild.

IN THE STUDIO OF...
A WILDLIFE ILLUSTRATOR

Ever since his first publication appeared, Terence Lambert's illustrations have been in constant demand. Readers of the *Wildlife Fact-File*, to which he regularly contributes, will be familiar with his highly detailed style. Terence also undertakes private commissions and has recently completed 20 watercolours for the Sultan of Oman's summer palace.

Secluded from his family in a converted barn that now acts as his studio, Terence spends over 12 hours a day working on the bird paintings that have earned him his reputation as one of the country's foremost wildlife illustrators. His enthusiasm for all forms of wildlife is immense: lines of stuffed birds are suspended from wooden rods in his studio. Earlier collections of birds line the drawers of huge wooden chests and, as he pulls open each drawer, the smell of mothballs lingers in the air.

The specimens are just one part of his struggle for perfection. Careful reference to them, and to his vast collection of slides, ensures that his illustrations are feather-perfect. In one corner of his studio stands his latest completed commission: a peregrine falcon perched upon a lichen-clad rock. His attention to detail extends to every part of the canvas: the lichen is carefully researched to make sure that it is a species that grows in the falcon's preferred habitat. Terence holds the view that every last blade of grass counts. He points to the bottom of the picture and claims that 'if you don't care about the brush-strokes down here then it detracts from the whole work'. A true craftsman, he enjoys the challenge of using simple tools and techniques to master the difficult medium of watercolours, and dismisses short cuts.

With each commission Terence tries to say something new and fresh, constantly looking for a detail that will arrest the viewer. In one recent work the blades of grass between the talons of a Montagu's harrier told the story of a viper snatched from the ground. Often it is the detail that provides the inspiration for the rest of the work. Terence is constantly finding new angles from which to depict his subjects and tries not to portray birds in profile. Most of his paintings depict scenes that it would be difficult to photograph.

Terence's constant quest to provide a fresh view or what he calls 'a peg to hang the pictures on' has earned him criticism in the past: Sir Peter Scott remarked that he was looking too hard for a clever idea, often at the expense of the subject. An earlier work was said to be 'too photographic'. Today his style

Below: Terence is a perfectionist, and as a result very rarely completely satisfied with his finished work. The faults in each picture remain 'like bits of spinach lodged between the teeth'.

Left: It is his need to define every
claw and every feather that
makes Terence an illustrator
rather than an artist. An artist, he
feels, would be happy to lose
some of the detail in shadow.

is slightly freer and the feathers, he says, 'have more air in them'. When asked whether he ever considers adopting a different approach, he expresses the view that this would be 'dishonest'. He describes how many illustrators are achieving a similar style via photorealism: they enlarge a photograph to the size of the canvas and trace in the required details. Although the results are often impressive, Terence likens their technique to painting by numbers. It is, he says, 'like a woodcarver who uses machines'.

Terence is dismissive of his own success. Although his paintings have been in constant demand over the last 15 years, he does not believe that he has yet mastered his craft. As he points to a scene of two pheasants roosting he reveals that there are very few works with which he feels completely satisfied. He traces the line of feathers with his finger, attempting to show that the seemingly perfect set of feathers is wrongly aligned.

Terence Lambert's entry into the profession of artist was unconventional. His love of natural history was apparent at an early age — one of his earliest memories is of looking into a turtle dove's nest. The drawing came later, after watching his father sketch a carrot in his brother's exercise book. At nine years of age he beat adult entrants to win a drawing competition. For a young boy captivated by the beauty of the natural world, painting was a means of being able to 'possess' the living things that attracted him.

Coming from a family of welders, however, the progression to wildlife illustrator was by no means a natural one for Terence. With only one O level, in woodwork, he was not automatically qualified to enter art school, but was accepted after sitting an entrance examination. To justify his chosen career to his parents, Terence opted for a course in industrial design. During this training he never touched a paint palette. He was finally dissuaded from a career as a product designer during an interview with

Left: Terence's studio is filled with stuffed birds. The victims of storms or road accidents, they provide a valuable source of detailed reference.

extensive knowledge of birds is often involved in this decision: for the painting of the peregrine falcon he referred to a cabinet specimen for much of the detail but realized that, because the bird was from an aviary, its bill was much longer than that of its wild counterpart.

Rather than concentrating on one work at a time, Terence prefers to have as many as four or five illustrations on the go at once. The larger private commissions are usually completed during daylight hours, while the illustrations are often worked on under artificial light.

For each work Terence carefully details every feather and mark in pencil before beginning to paint. Terence admits that if he dwelled on this arduous task before he began, he would probably never embark on the process again. His illustrator's eye is constantly applied to the world around him. He spends much time 'loitering', especially in the vicinity of the barn owls he keeps. Although the sight of them gliding above his home is familiar, it is still one in which he can become utterly absorbed. He recalls a river in Scotland the beauty of which could literally reduce him to tears. The natural world always takes precedence over the manufactured one for Terence, who dismisses his own illustrations as 'weak efforts' that will only be of true value when they 'fly off the board'.

To anyone thinking of following in his footsteps, Terence advises starting young so as not miss the opportunity to exploit their youthful imagination. Unfortunately, he says, many talented young artists lose their vocation by following a trade and resuming art only when it is too late. While publishers clamour for his work and lesser illustrators envy his talent, Terence remains unmoved by the fuss. He lives in mid-Wales with his wife and four daughters, just 'earning a living'.

Suzanne Jones

the manager of a manufacturing firm in Uxbridge. The interviewer caught sight of one of his bird illustrations among a portfolio of technical drawings and told him that as a product designer his talents would be wasted. Three years after this incident his work was noticed by Billy Collins (of Harper Collins, the publishers) at an exhibition for wildlife illustrators. Terence was immediately commissioned for his first book.

Terence regards the skill of drawing as the basis of his craft. The mistakes he identifies in his work today are nearly always a result of errors at the drawing stage. He has a keen eye for the methods used to apply paint and says that he learned 'on the job'. He has always used simple tools; until recently he relied upon a child's set of watercolours. His only extravagance is with new brushes.

Terence Lambert has a natural disregard for rules and believes that there is 'no tablet of stone that tells you how to paint'. He combines pure watercolour techniques, which allow the paper to show through, with overpainting in gouache. He has his own self-imposed set of disciplines, however; he will not copy completely from a cabinet specimen or a transparency. His

Opposite: Terence's paintings develop from tiny thumbnail sketches that he roughs out on tracing paper. These provide a basis for him to build on. He paints his backgrounds after he has completed the main subject, often working to within a millimetre of the central bird and allowing the paint to creep through the paper to close the gap. He then fills in the boxes left for small details.

ON LOCATION WITH...
A WILDLIFE FILM-MAKER

Opposite: Queen of the Beasts was Richard's second film and the result of 18 months spent working in the Serengeti. The countless hours patiently devoted to the project reaped their reward as he captured remarkable footage showing acts of infanticide among lions which had never been seen on film before.

Overleaf: Richard believes that it is best to start making films about an area in which you have specialized knowledge. Much of his work so far has been about the wildlife of east Africa, where he grew up.

Below: It takes guts, imagination and an obsessive dedication to make it to the top in the rat race world of the wildlife film-maker. Richard Matthews has got all this and more.

Seven years ago a young assistant producer at the BBC Natural History Unit gave up his job and mortgaged his home to make his first film. The producer was Richard Matthews and the film, *The Secret Leopard*, was an immediate success, launching his career as a wildlife film-maker.

Richard had been working on programmes such as *The Natural World* for the BBC and had produced a programme for David Attenborough's series *The Living Planet*. Frustrated that he was missing out on all the excitement, Richard decided he would rather be behind the camera watching wildlife than organizing the production team. A casual remark at a drinks party prompted him into action when he learned that a leopard and her cubs were regularly being seen in the Maasai Mara Game Reserve in Kenya. Within three days, Richard had decided to try to finance and produce his first film.

Six weeks later Richard was in the Maasai Mara ready to begin filming. Samantha Purdy joined him as his assistant. They hardly knew

each other, having met only a few weeks previously, but shared a love for east African wildlife. Richard had converted a small four-wheel-drive van for filming. One of the doors was removed, and the cramped interior forced him to sit with his legs swinging over the edge, covered by a sheet of canvas to avoid disturbing the wildlife. Samantha drove while Richard searched for game to film and shouted directions.

To compensate for his lack of experience in predicting the behaviour of the game, Richard decided to track the leopard for as long as possible. Their day began at 4 a.m. and ended when the light failed. It was this constant persistence that resulted in memorable scenes such as the leopard's struggle to drag a zebra it had just killed away from the eyes of scavenging hyenas.

Lack of experience certainly provided some close shaves for Richard, who in the first week of filming found himself face to face with an angry hippopotamus. He spotted the injured hippo lying on the ground and crawled towards it in the hope of filming some impressive low-angle shots. What he had not realized was that the wide-angle lens on his 16mm film camera was deceptive after the 35mm still camera he was used to, and made the animal appear much further away than it really was. Within minutes the hippo was charging towards the startled cameraman. He dodged, and the hippo charged past him to the jeep where it took a chunk out of the bonnet. Even at such a nerve-racking moment, Richard was confident that what he was doing in life was right. He had invested everything he had in the film and was determined that it would be a success.

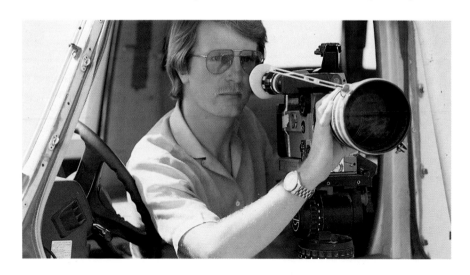

Opposite: For the lover of east African wildlife, the opportunity to witness and enjoy at first hand the breathtaking beauty of the animals and landscape in which they live will offer its own compensations for the extremely arduous and often uncomfortable life of the film-maker.

Below: A group of hippopotamuses filmed from a distance as they enjoy an early morning bath might seem harmless enough. They make a rather more alarming proposition, however, when they appear in the viewfinder, charging at speed towards the cameraman who is armed with nothing more than a wide-angle lens.

His dedication paid off: *The Secret Leopard* won several awards and was bought by *National Geographic* and Survival Anglia.

To avoid being plagued by the tourists who had on occasion caused him to miss sequences while filming in the Maasai Mara, Richard chose to make his next film, *Queen of the Beasts*, in the Serengeti. Although there have been many films on lions, most concentrate on their hunting skills, and despite discouragement from other film-makers Richard felt there was still much to be said about their social behaviour. Some unique footage resulted from 18 months spent filming 50 lions, including the first-ever shots of infanticide among lions.

The filming of the infanticide was the result of following a lioness and her three cubs for over six weeks, often spending five days at a time away from the base camp. It was a gruesome incident. A group of lionesses moved on to the territory of another female and chased her away from her cubs, while a male lion crept up to kill the cubs, eating two and leaving the other for the vultures. The purpose of infanticide is to remove the cubs from a female so that she is ready to mate (a female

with cubs will not mate again until her offspring are around 18 months old), and 24 hours later Richard was amazed to see the lioness, who had come into heat, mating with the same male that had eaten her cubs.

To ensure that *Queen of the Beasts* provided new and different images of lions, Richard designed a coffin-like construction that allowed him to get very low-angle shots from only 15cm above ground level using a wide-angle lens. He spent hours unable to move within the confines of the narrow box, often in extremely high temperatures. First, however, it was essential to get the lions used to the contraption, since he was protected only by chicken wire.

The risks of filming are always carefully calculated and Richard does not believe that the profession of wildlife film-maker is necessarily a dangerous one. Richard's quest to provide a fresh look at lions was certainly successful — the film was acclaimed for its unusual images and even established film-makers agreed that they had learned from it.

Filming is often a tense and absorbing process and Richard's response to missing a sequence is likely to be volatile. It was for this reason that he decided to modify his jeep so that he could both film and drive for his next film, *Kingdom of the Black God*. This is a study of the Ngorongoro crater in Tanzania. The crater, which is 20km across and enclosed by steep slopes, is brimming with wildlife and had provided some of the best sequences for *Queen of the Beasts*. There had been only one other film about the crater, in the 1970s, and Richard felt that there was still much to say. The film, due to be released at the end of 1991, depicts many scenes which have not been shot before, including a lioness confronting a hippo.

Once filming is complete Richard returns home to edit — a process which can take several months. His approach changed dramatically as a result of discussions with film producer and wildlife photographer John

Downer, who made the BBC Natural History Unit's series *Supersense*. John encouraged Richard to start with the shots which provided the most impact, building the rest of the film around them.

There is no doubt that Richard is a complete workaholic, obsessed with making exceptionally good wildlife films. Describing today's world of film-making as a rat race, he expresses the view that the profession can be entered only by those with complete determination to overcome every hurdle. A passion for wildlife is essential and a formal qualification in the subject helps — Richard has a BSc in life sciences. Young enthusiasts can contact organizations like the International Association of Wildlife Film-Makers.

Richard plans to make more films all over the world, and hopes that some will be three- or six-part series which have a greater impact on the audience. Having made three films in grasslands, he would like to move to different habitats and lists mountains and snow as among his top priorities. Whatever the hurdles, he is emphatic that he 'wouldn't give it up for anything'.

Suzanne Jones

Below: Much of the footage for *Queen of the Beasts* was shot from within a narrow box covered in chicken wire and attached to the front of his jeep. Richard believes that techniques of this nature are essential in order to satisfy today's increasingly demanding audiences.

THROUGH THE LENS OF AN...
AMATEUR PHOTOGRAPHER

For the past four years the name Charlie Hamilton-James has been synonymous with success at the annual Wildlife Photographer of the Year Awards, sponsored by British Gas and BBC *Wildlife* magazine. It all began in 1988 when the 14-year-old Charlie was awarded third prize in the junior section of the competition for a photograph of a kingfisher sitting on a perch near its nest hole. In 1990 film-maker Simon King described the shot that earned Charlie the title Young Wildlife Photographer of the Year as displaying 'the photographer's ability to transform the ordinary into the extraordinary'. The scene referred to was of two young wild rabbits which Charlie had photographed after slowly edging on his stomach to within 3m of them. That same year he also received second prize for a picture of an otter feeding on a lumpsucker fish.

In November 1991, Charlie was again awarded the title Wildlife Photographer of the Year for a shot of the otters that have captivated him during his annual pilgrimages to Shetland. Charlie admits to being obsessed by this windswept group of islands that offers the largest population of otters to be found anywhere in Britain.

The islands occupy the most northerly position of any group in Britain, and the climate is, not surprisingly, extremely cold and windy. The otters, however, more than compensate for the harsh conditions — and their timetable particularly endears them to a young photographer. Unlike their nocturnal relatives on the mainland, they prefer to hunt for food during the hours of daylight and this, says Charlie, means that he does not have to get up at four in the morning. Instead he patrols the same 16-km stretch of coastline each day, setting off at 10 a.m. and returning around mid-afternoon. His walk extends across the territories of one male and three female otters.

Even if he does not glimpse an otter, there is plenty of wildlife to capture his attention. Shetland boasts a huge bird population that includes terns, whimbrels and divers. Seals haul out on the rocks and the local population of sheep numbers thousands — for a young wildlife photographer who is not afraid of the cold it is paradise.

It is essential to be downwind of the otter, Charlie says, if you are to avoid having your scent picked up. Otters prefer to hunt for food when the incoming tide is still quite some distance from the shore and this, he believes, is the best time to try to creep

Below: Charlie has been photographing wildlife since he was given his first camera at the age of 13. He has already won many awards and considerable critical acclaim for his work and hopes one day to realize an ambition to become a wildlife cameraman with the BBC.

Above: Charlie makes an annual pilgrimage to the Shetland Islands, where he spends time studying and photographing Britain's largest population of otters. This shot won him second prize in the 1990 Young Wildlife Photographer of the Year awards. He was also awarded the first prize.

Left: Unlike the nocturnal otters in most parts of Britain, those on the Shetland Islands are more active and hunt for food by day. This makes photographing them a far less problematic and unsociable business.

Above: Patience and persistence are two key elements in becoming a successful wildlife photographer. It is often necessary to construct a hide many weeks before using it, and then to sit quietly inside for many hours before being rewarded with the chance to capture the planned sequence of shots.

to photograph a kingfisher diving) for his twelfth birthday. The following year he received a camera and was then able to record the group of kingfishers, not far from his home in Bristol, that were now occupying so much of his time. Charlie has picked up a few tips from David Boag and is now an expert in his own right.

Charlie is currently studying photography at Falmouth College of Art. Although he does not believe that a formal training is essential for a successful photographer, he says that it does speed up the learning process. He feels, however, that the most important quality for a wildlife photographer is persistence.

His immediate plans for the future include a two-year study of the behaviour of otters, which he intends to complete in Shetland. He would also like to study zoology at university and nurses an ambition one day to become a cameraman with the BBC Natural History Unit. However, 'I'm not qualified for either,' he says, referring to his few academic qualifications, for which 'kingfishers were to blame'.

Suzanne Jones

towards them. Able to detect only movement and silhouettes, the otters allow the patient and quiet photographer to get within centimetres of their sleek bodies. For Charlie, this has often involved edging over wet, seaweed-covered rocks.

Charlie thinks of himself as a naturalist first and he believes that all wildlife photographers must love their subjects. He was inspired at an early age to begin a five-year study of kingfishers after receiving a book by David Boag (who was the first person

Right: In order to take photographs of the highest quality, it is necessary to use a relatively short lens. The one Charlie favours is just 50mm, and this means that he must get extremely close to his subject. These rabbits were photographed from just 3m away.

Left: A good photograph will rarely betray the problems that may have been involved in the taking of it. Much of Charlie's finest work has resulted from hours spent edging slowly across wet rocks and lying motionless on remote, cold, damp and windswept hillsides.

PHOTOGRAPHING KINGFISHERS

Charlie Hamilton-James began to study kingfishers when he was 12 years old, after being given a book on diving kingfishers for his birthday. He has spent time with David Boag, the first person to photograph a kingfisher diving and the author of the book, and has picked up many useful tips from him.

This expertise led Charlie to spend three weeks with a BBC cameraman making a five-second sequence for David Attenborough's series Trials of Life. The episode focused on the hazards encountered by young eels (elvers) on their journey upriver. The required sequence, which was to be in slow motion, was of a kingfisher diving into the river to catch an elver. It was an unenviable task, particularly as kingfishers are not especially partial to elvers, and it called for a cunning strategy to make it work.

The sequence was to be taken from below, and this involved filming through the bottom of a fish tank. As the kingfisher showed a marked lack of interest in the elvers, a layer of clingfilm was stretched over the tank, which contained other fish. The elvers were then placed in a small pool of water on top of the clingfilm.

The final sequence, which took over three weeks to film, was particularly impressive because it was taken from an angle below the perched kingfisher. The kingfisher was shown hovering above the tank before diving through the clingfilm into the tank. The experience taught Charlie a great deal about how far he could 'push the kingfisher into the unnatural' without harming it in any way. At the culmination of filming he had managed to persuade the bird to fish through a layer of clingfilm from a fish tank supported on a silver coffee-table nearly 1m above the surface of the water.

TIPS FOR PHOTOGRAPHING KINGFISHERS

● Kingfishers are creatures of habit and are regularly seen along the same stretch of river.

● Each bird has its own territory which it uses for feeding purposes. With patience and careful observation it is possible to locate these territories. Look out for a branch coated in white droppings — it may be a favoured perch.

● Remember to keep the pool constantly stocked with fish.

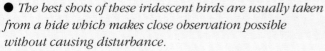

● The best shots of these iridescent birds are usually taken from a hide which makes close observation possible without causing disturbance.

● To ensure the safety of the hide and equipment, it is best to construct them on private land with the permission of the landowner.

● A good way of encouraging regular visits by the kingfisher is to construct a pool containing fish about 3–4m from the hide. Kingfishers prefer small fish such as minnows, gudgeon and bullheads which can be caught quite easily in a large net. About 50 or 60 of these small fish should be enough to attract the bird's attention.

● Construct a perch from which the kingfisher can dive close to the pool.

● You will need to be very patient when working in the hide as it may be hours or even days before you catch sight of a kingfisher. It may also take some time for the bird to become accustomed to fishing from the pool.

CALENDAR OF EVENTS

JANUARY '90

A MEETING in Moscow of 700 religious leaders and parliamentarians from over 30 countries discusses green issues and President Gorbachev calls for an 'international Green Cross' to aid all nations with ecological problems. He also proposes the creation of a United Nations (UN) force of 'green berets' to intervene in ecological disasters.

European ski resorts suffer lack of snow for third consecutive year. Concern rises that this may be a sign of climatic change.

1 Morocco threatened by 300sq km oil slick from Iranian tanker, *Kharg-5*, but oil later dispersed with little damage to coastline.

9 'Mad cow disease' or Bovine Spongiform Encephalopathy (BSE) causes 600 new cases each month, and the British government announces an extra £2.2m for research.

19 CITES ban on commercial ivory trade comes into force, preventing international trade between CITES member states, except for a few southern African and Asian countries that were not included in the ban.

25 Hurricane-force winds gusting to 160km/h kill 46 people in southern Britain.

FEBRUARY '90

10 Two red kites found dead from poisoning in Scotland. In 1989 the RSPB and NCC reintroduced five birds into Scotland and six into England, a century after they last bred there. About 200 birds remain in Wales.

15 A National Farmers' Union meeting passed a resolution rejecting organic farming methods in favour of continued use of chemicals.

17 A fire destroys 70 per cent of the Poca Das Antas Nature Reserve in Brazil, putting at risk the survival of the golden lion tamarin (one of the world's rarest monkeys).

21 A 24km stretch of Sussex coast is closed to bathers after six containers of toxic potassium cyanide are washed ashore.

26 Environmentalists stage protest at Twyford Down near Winchester, Hampshire, where a beauty spot is threatened by construction of a six-lane motorway.

27 Exxon Corporation and Exxon Shipping are indicted on five criminal charges relating to the 1989 Alaskan oil spill.

MARCH '90

ILLEGAL logging in the Korup National Park in Cameroon causes concern to the World Wide Fund for Nature (WWF), which has established a joint venture with the Cameroon government to promote sustainable use of the tropical rainforest.

Third international North Sea Conference at The Hague results in agreement to reduce by at least one half the levels of pollution from the 37 worst pollutants. Levels of lead, mercury, cadmium and dioxin to be cut by at least 70 per cent by 1995.

5 The UK government announces that Britain will end the dumping of sewage sludge in the North Sea by 1998. Current level is 300 million tonnes per year.

13 Brazil creates three new reserves with a combined area of over 16,000sq km in Amazonia where rubber tapping will be favoured and all predatory use of the rainforest (e.g. deforestation) will be prohibited.

23 Market research conducted over the past year indicates the scope of the green consumer boom. Over a 20-week period, 14 per cent of 6300 households bought a product on a designated 'green' list. Very few of these purchasers were 'brand loyal'.

APRIL '90

A CONFERENCE in Washington on climatic change is attended by delegates from 17 governments. President Bush tells the gathering that more research is needed first and France's Brice Lalonde (Secretary of State for the Environment) criticizes the US government for not allowing all the nations to contribute equally to the debate.

7 Coto Doñana National Park in southern Spain is threatened with plans to build a leisure complex at the edge of the reserve.

21 Freak floods in Queensland, New South Wales and Victoria, Australia, cover 2.6 million sq km in areas which were affected by drought only a few weeks before.

22 Earth Day 1990 sees an estimated 200 million people involved in worldwide demonstrations, celebrations and tree plantings.

26 Earthquake in Qinghai Province, central China, kills 115 people.

27 The fourth anniversary of the nuclear accident at Chernobyl is marked by tens of thousands of people in the Soviet republics of Ukraine and Byelorussia. An estimated 300 people have died from nuclear-related disorders since the explosion, which cost 31 lives at the time.

MAY '90

Most European TV networks co-operate to produce a week-long selection of environmental and conservation programmes under the title One World Week.

9 A cyclone in Andhra Pradesh, India, kills 220 and leaves 3 million homeless.

16 United Nations Environmental Conference in Bergen, Norway ends with 34 countries signing an agreement to 'anticipate, prevent and attack the causes of environmental degradation', including global warming and ozone depletion. Carbon dioxide emission targets are to be set in November 1990.

28 Britain is to be taken to court over three polluted Lancashire beaches (Southport, Formby and Blackpool) which fail to meet European Community (EC) standards. Acceptable minimum standards for bathing were laid down in a 1975 directive which was implemented in 1985.

30 Peru hit by earthquake, which killed 101 people. Romania also hit by an earthquake (6.9 on the Richter scale) centred 240km north-east of Bucharest. Very little surface damage.

JUNE '90

EC commissioner responsible for environmental affairs, Carlos Ripa di Meana, announces proposals requiring companies to undertake annual reviews of environmental management practices throughout their operations.

11 US coastline threatened following a fire on board a tanker in the Gulf of Mexico carrying 173 million litres of crude oil. The Norwegian vessel *Mega Borg* is carrying more than three times as much oil as the *Exxon Valdez* spilt in Alaska the previous year.

22 More than 40,000 estimated dead in an earthquake that strikes 260sq km of north-west Iran (epicentre in Caspian Sea). EC offers $1m (£0.6m) in instant aid.

27 The 58 signatories of the Ramsar Convention on Wetlands meet in Geneva to agree to further measures to protect the world's most important wetlands. A new fund of SwFr 20,000 (£8000) is established to aid conservation of wetlands in developing countries.

29 In London, 97 governments agree to strengthen the 1987 Montreal Protocol, which calls for the phasing out of ozone-destroying chlorofluorocarbons (CFCs) by the year 2000. A global fund of $160m (£94m) is established, with scope for more money as new countries participate.

JULY '90

Plantlife launches the second in its series of meadow purchases sponsored by the pharmaceutical company Timotei. Meadows are one of the most threatened traditional rural habitats in Britain.

9 A 24km stretch of Cumbrian coastline is declared unsafe after items contaminated by the 1983 Sellafield radiation leak are washed ashore.

16 Earthquake of 7.7 on the Richter scale hits 96km north of Manila killing at least 600 people and leaving 2600 homeless.

18 Japan agrees to suspend driftnet fishing in the south Pacific for the 1990–91 season. A United Nations (UN) resolution banning the use of driftnets comes into force in 1991.

26 The EC agriculture minister announces that the community will pay farmers to limit environmental damage and will encourage diversification through the payment of increased subsidies. The moves require ratification by EC farm ministers.

27 UK National Rivers Authority announces tough controls on pollution, especially for sewage and industrial waste emitted into waterways.

AUGUST '90

2 Iraqi troops and aircraft seize control of Kuwait. Oil prices jump to $26 (£15.30) per barrel.

3 Measures to protect the few remaining French Pyrenean bears are announced by the French government. Only about 12 bears now remain, compared with 70 or so in 1957.

3 Britain has its hottest day since weather records began: Cheltenham 37.1°C (98.8°F), London 35°C (95°F).

16 The Council for National Parks calls for the designation of four new national parks — South Downs, North Pennines, New Forest and Cambrian Mountains — in order to protect these much visited regions.

16 The US Federal Court rules that the Endangered Species Act covering wildlife in the US will now also apply to plants and animals worldwide if they are adversely affected by federally-funded projects.

23 Countryside Commission publishes its first review for 10 years, calling for new and urgent action to be taken to protect Britain's areas of outstanding natural beauty.

SEPTEMBER '90

11 Heavy rainfall in vicinity of Seoul in South Korea results in severe flooding and more than 77 people dead.

25 Chris Patten, Environment Secretary, launches the government's 300-page White Paper *This Common Inheritance*. Proposals include the 'greening' of Whitehall, a new MOT test on carbon monoxide emissions from cars and heavier fines for water pollution. Critics identify lack of commitment to improving public transport, and no new initiatives to cut carbon emissions and CFCs.

OCTOBER '90

29 Second World Climate Conference held in Geneva, organized by the World Meteorological Organization (WMO), fails to agree emission standards for carbon dioxide but does result in 137 participating governments signing an agreement recognizing the threat of global warming and pledging to take steps to limit it. King Hussein of Jordan warns delegates that the environmental impact of a Gulf war would be 'swift, severe and devastating'. Conference lasts until 7 November.

NOVEMBER '90

1 Environmental Protection Act comes into effect. Under Section 138, the Nature Conservancy Council

(NCC) ceases to exist and is replaced by three new bodies: English Nature, the NCC for Scotland (which in April 1992 will fuse with the Countryside Commission for Scotland to become Scottish National Heritage) and the Countryside Council for Wales.

28 National Tree Week launch with the aim to plant 1990 trees throughout Britain.

DECEMBER '90

US CLIMATE Analysis Centre reports that rainfall is 75 per cent of normal in western Sahel and less than half the norm in eastern Sudan and northern Ethiopia. Drought and pest damage reduce harvests to as low as those of 1984–85 and estimates suggest that as many as 12 million people in Ethiopia and Sudan may suffer famine.

EC countries agree to phase out the production of all CFCs by the year 1997.

17 Friends of the Earth nominates Eastern Electricity for its 'Green Con of the Year' prize for claiming that using more electricity will stop global warming.

JANUARY '91

12 The British government pledges to review planning procedures which allow the development of important wildlife sites. In particular it will look at the case of Canford Heath in Dorset where a site of special scientific interest (SSSI) is under threat from a housing development.

26 First images broadcast worldwide of oil slick emanating from the Sea Island terminal and bombed Al Khafji terminal in the Gulf. Cormorants and black-necked grebes are the first victims, but also threatened are the millions of migratory birds which use the area's mudflats

and islands as a resting ground between Africa and Siberia.

27 'Peatland in Peril', a weekend of events and conference on peatland habitats and how to conserve them, is held at the Wildfowl and Wetlands Trust at Slimbridge.

30 The government of Taiwan publicly burns confiscated wildlife products including over 350kg of raw and worked ivory, 4kg of rhinoceros horn, 200 turtleshell spectacle frames and assorted skins. This is the third public burning by Taiwan of confiscated wildlife products.

FEBRUARY '91

21 Hundreds of Kuwaiti oil wells are set alight by Iraqi troops. Greenpeace protesters are removed from the Iraqi Embassy in Rome following a protest against the use of the environment as a weapon of war.

Natural Environment Research Council (NERC) approves a special topic research programme in wildlife disease, with the majority of funding becoming available in April 1992.

Friends of Animals ships 41 US army vehicles to African wildlife agencies, primarily for use in elephant protection.

MARCH '91

UP TO 1000 oil wells burning in Kuwait. The first fires extinguished after burning for one month. An international team including the International Council for Bird Preservation (ICBP) in Saudi Arabia lists 14 critical sites in the Gulf requiring aid and the first consignments of specialist clean-up equipment are flown into the region.

In Botswana's Okavango Delta a water extraction scheme is suspended after local people protest against the proposal.

6 David Bellamy plants the one millionth tree on behalf of the British Trust for Conservation Volunteers (BTCV) since the Trust began its tree planting programme in 1987.

7 Greenpeace launches *Solo*, the eighth ship in its international fleet.

13 A wildlife site of international importance, Canford Heath in Dorset, is saved from developers by the intervention of the Secretary of State for the Environment, Michael Heseltine.

18 EC council adopts amendments to the 1975 Waste Management Directive, which will provide a foundation for new legislation concerning recycling and resource recovery.

19 'What on Earth is to be done?', an international conference on the next generation of environment and development challenges, organized by the International Institute for Environment and Development and *The Observer* newspaper, is held in London.

27 Construction begins on Europe's first wildlife teaching hospital at Aylesbury close to its parent hospital for treating wild animals, St Tiggywinkles, where 8000 animals are treated each year.

APRIL '91

15 Food and Agriculture Organization (FAO) of the UN organizes a five-day conference on Environment and Agriculture in 's Hertogenbosch, Netherlands, attended by 250 experts from 124 countries.

21 WWF launches a campaign to end the trade in rhinoceros products. Only 11,000 rhinos are thought to remain worldwide, a decline of 85 per cent over the last 30 years.

22 World Bank officials meet Non-Governmental Organization (NGO) officials to discuss the World Bank's envi-

ronmental policies since 1989 in a four-day meeting.

30 A 50-year mining ban is declared in the Antarctic by a majority of the 39 nations who have signed the 1959 Antarctic Treaty. (The member nations meet again in October 1991 to ratify the ban.)

French protesters win their campaign to stop the construction of a barrage at Serre de la Fare on the Loire near Le Puy with a ruling from the French government that the area should remain in its natural state. The result is regarded as a classic environmental campaigning success that combined a vigorous international media campaign, direct action that prevented construction from beginning, and a successful legal challenge to the local prefect's ruling.

MAY '91

1 The World Meteorological Organization (WMO) opens its 11th Congress in Geneva which runs until the 25th. Establishment of the Global Climate Observing System (GCOS) to provide observations for monitoring climate and detecting climatic change.

11 National Environment Week begins. With over 2000 events nationwide, it is organized by the Civic Trust in association with voluntary environmental groups, schools, businesses and local authorities. Events include cleaning up canals, building bat-boxes and conserving churchyards for wildlife.

18 National Wildflower Week, organized by the Royal Society for Nature Conservation (RSNC), begins.

The annual meeting of the International Whaling Commission (IWC) in Reykjavik ends with the commercial whaling moratorium in place but no agreement regarding catch quotas for whaling nations, nor on scientific whaling. Iceland threatens to leave the IWC.

JUNE '91

A SPECIAL trust fund is set up by the United Nations Environment Programme (UNEP) to develop and coordinate a plan to assess and deal with the damage caused by the Gulf War. Participating organizations include the International Union for the Conservation of Nature (IUCN) and WWF. Japan is the first to contribute to the fund with a grant of $1.11 million (£650,000).

500 oil wells still burning in the Gulf and estimates are that 7–8 million barrels of oil have been discharged into the sea.

Prime Minister Haughey of Ireland declares all seas around Ireland as a whale and dolphin sanctuary — the first such sanctuary to be declared by a European country. This makes hunting of all species of cetaceans illegal within a 320km limit.

5 World Environment Day is celebrated worldwide, with climatic change as this year's theme. Public endorsement by world leaders of a report entitled 'Common Responsibility in the 1990s — the Stockholm Initiative on Global Security and Governance'.

20 Five countries of southern Africa (Botswana, Malawi, Namibia, Zambia and Zimbabwe) sign an agreement to establish a centre for marketing elephant ivory legally. Reactions are sought from CITES and other relevant governments, institutions and organizations.

21 Working conference on the environment, in Prague, with the environment ministers of most European countries as well as Canada, Japan and the US.

JULY '91

THE 47 member-countries of the International Tropical Timber Organization (ITTO) conclude their meeting in Quito having made some progress, but leaving many key issues unresolved.

6 The week-long *Sunday Times* Environment, Wildlife and Conservation Exhibition supported by RSNC opens at Olympia, London.

7 Welsh WATCH Day at the United Counties Showground near Camarthen, Dyfed. Includes participation of all the Welsh Wildlife Trusts.

8 Prime Minister John Major announces the establishment of a unified environment agency to monitor the state of air and water and to regulate emissions and discharges. Details to be proposed later.

14 National WATCH Day at Ferry Meadows, near Peterborough. Action and games with David Bellamy and Chris Packham.

15 The Annual G-7 Conference opens in London. Environment and development issues form an important part of three days of discussion.

15 Michael Heseltine, Environment Secretary, announces new initiatives on waste recycling. The government's aim remains to recycle 25 per cent of all household waste by the end of the century.

AUGUST '91

19 World Congress of the International Solar Energy Society opens in Denver, Colorado, USA. It runs until 23rd.

25 This year's four-day International Symposium on Energy and the Environment opens in Espoo, Finland.

SEPTEMBER '91

1 Wildlife & Countryside (Amendment) Act 1991. This creates a new offence if a person 'knowingly causes or permits the illegal killing of any wild bird or animal' (thus closing a loophole in the law allowing gamekeepers to kill birds of prey).

11 WWF celebrates 30 years of worldwide conservation work and launches its Go Wild Club for 7–18 year olds.

11 The International Wildlife Film Makers' Symposium 1991 opens. The theme is: 'Towards 2000'. It runs until 15th and is held at the University of Bath, Avon.

23 Two-day European Environment Conference held at the University of Nottingham to discuss environmental policy and practice.

23 In a survey lasting until 4 October, Coastwatch UK monitors pollution along the UK coastline, sponsored by Norwich Union and organized by the Marine Conservation Society.

24 European Waste Policy Conference in London, to discuss the waste management policy of the EC.

25 The Plantlife Peat Inquiry into peatland conservation holds the first of three public hearings which will provide material and evidence before a National Peatland Survey is published in 1992.

25 Two-day European Parliament conference on the theme 'Nature Conservation — Europe 2000' opens. It is organized together with WWF.

30 Start of Ele-week, a week of fundraising activity organized by Elefriends.

OCTOBER '91

3 International three-day Conference on 'La Vie de l'Eau et l'Eau de la Vie' opens under the auspices of the EC, the World Health Organization (WHO) and the Luxembourg government, in Luxembourg.

4 Antarctic Treaty Nations meet in Madrid, Spain.

6 WWF Walk for Species in Danger. 400 sponsored walks across the UK to raise money for nature.

21 Launch of 'Caring for the World — A Strategy for Conservation and Development' by the World Conservation Union (WCU), in cities worldwide.

NOVEMBER '91

28 National Tree Week begins. Last year 700,000 trees were planted during the course of the year.

A two-month exhibition opens at the Natural History Museum in London. Wildlife Photographer of the Year Competition results are on show. Organized with BBC *Wildlife* Magazine and the Fauna and Flora Preservation Society, and sponsored by British Gas. Later touring the UK and selected overseas venues.

EVENTS IN 1992

JANUARY
International Conference on Water and the Environment in Dublin.

FEBRUARY
Fourth World Conference on National Parks and Protected Areas held in Caracas, Venezuela, 10th to 21st.

MARCH
CITES first biannual meeting for the year will be held in Japan.

JUNE
United Nations Conference on Environment and Development ('The Earth Summit'), in Rio de Janeiro, Brazil, 1st to 12th.

DIRECTORY OF ORGANIZATIONS

GLOBAL ORGANIZATIONS AND INITIATIVES

Ark Environmental Foundation
PO Box 1784
London W9 3QW
℡ 081 968 6780
Provides information and a framework for environmentally positive community action to benefit the natural environment.

Cat Survival Trust
The Centre
Codicote Road
Welwyn
Hertfordshire AL6 9TU
℡ 0438 716873
Conservation and breeding of endangered cats worldwide.

Council of Europe
Centre Naturopa
Conseil de l'Europe
BP 431 R 6
F 67006 Strasbourg
France
℡ 010 33 88 61 49 61
Steering committee for Conservation and Management of the Environment and Natural Resources.

Earthwatch (Europe)
Belsyre Court
57 Woodstock Road
Oxford OX2 6HU
℡ 0865 311600
Runs scientific field research projects worldwide using volunteers who share costs and work with professionals.

Environmental Investigation Agency
208–209 Upper Street
London N1 1RL
℡ 071 704 9441
Worldwide environmental monitoring agency.

European Commission DG X1 (Environment)
Division B3 EC
Rue de la Loi 200
1049 Brussels
Belgium
Responsible for EC environmental policy.

European Institute of Ecology
1 Rue des Recollets
BP 4005 – 57040
Metz
Cedex
France

Fauna and Flora Preservation Society
c/o Zoological Society of London
Regents Park
London NW1 4RY
℡ 071 387 9656
Conservation of wild animals and wild plants worldwide.

Friends of the Earth International
Veriniging Milieudefensie
Tacovanden Heiligenberg
Damrak 26
1012 LJ Amsterdam
The Netherlands
℡ 3120 622 1366
International pressure group campaigning for protection of the environment and promotion of sustainable alternative sources of fuel and economic activity.

Gaia Foundation
18 Well Walk
London NW3 1LD
℡ 071 435 5000
Provides funding to support indigenous populations, mainly in the South American rainforest.

Greenpeace International
Keizersgracht 176
1610 DW Amsterdam
The Netherlands
℡ 010 31 205 236555
Campaigns against abuse of the environment through lobbying and non-violent direct action protests.

Groundwork Foundation
Bennetts Court
6 Bennetts Hill
Birmingham B2 5ST
℡ 021 236 8565
Restores landscapes and habitats on a local level, especially urban wastelands, working with communities, businesses and local authorities.

Institute for European Environmental Policy (IEEP)
3 Endsleigh Street
London WC1H 0DD
℡ 071 388 2117
Analyses and reports on environmental policy in Europe and promotes awareness of environment protection.

Institute of Terrestrial Ecology
Monks Wood Experimental Station
Abbots Ripton
Huntington PE17 2LS
℡ 04873 381
Research into ecosystems, surveys of landuse and vegetation and investigation into environmental problem areas.

International Council for Bird Preservation (ICBP)
32 Cambridge Road
Girton
Cambridge CB3 0PJ
℡ 0223 277318
Protection of the world's birds and their habitats.

International Dolphin Watch
Parklands
North Ferriby
Hull
Humberside HU14 3ET
Coordinates sightings of dolphins and porpoises and observations of their behaviour.

International Foundation for the Conservation of Birds
11300 Weddington Street
North Hollywood
California 91601
USA
Bird conservation in the US and the rest of the world.

International League for the Protection of Cetaceans (ILPC)
2 Meryon Court
Rye
East Sussex TN31 7LY
℡ 0797 223649
Protects and conserves whales, dolphins and porpoises, conducts and sponsors scientific research.

International Primate Protection League (IPPL)
116 Judd Street
London WC1H 9NS
℡ 071 837 7227
Works exclusively to protect primates (apes, lemurs, monkeys etc).

International Waterfowl and Wetlands Research Bureau (IWRB)
Slimbridge
Gloucestershire GL2 7BT
℡ 0453 890333
Promotes scientific research and the conservation of wetlands and their waterfowl populations.

International Whaling Commission
135 Station Road
Histon
Cambridge CB4 4NP
℡ 0223 233971
An intergovernmental organization which reviews measures to protect whales. Collects and disseminates data on whales.

International Wildlife Coalition (UK)
PO Box 73
Hartfield
Sussex TN7 4EY
℡ 034 2825482
Scientific research into wildlife and natural habitat destruction.

People's Trust for Endangered Species
Suite 9 Hamble House
Mead Row
Godalming
Surrey GU7 3JX
℡ 0483 424848
Aims to conserve and protect the environment through the protection of animals, plants and wild places.

Population Concern
231 Tottenham Court Road
London W1P 9AE
℡ 071 631 1546
Concerned with raising the awareness of the dangers of population growth, and promotes planned parenthood.

Rainforest Foundation
5 Fitzroy Lodge
The Grove
Highgate
London N6 5JU
℡ 071 348 2926
Protection of large areas of Amazonia and its natural inhabitants.

Society for Wildlife Art of the Nations
Wallsworth Hall
Sandhurst
Gloucestershire GL2 9PA
℡ 0452 731422
Aims to link artists with the cause of conservation of nature.

Survival International
310 Edgware Road
London W2 1DY
℡ 071 723 5535
Works for the rights of threatened tribal people and promotes their traditional sustainable way of life.

United Nations Ecology Programme (UNEP) UK
3 Endsleigh Street
London WC1H 0DD
℡ 071 388 2117
Monitors and assesses changes in the world's physical (human and natural) state. Coordinates and promotes action by the international community.

World Conservation Monitoring Centre
219c Huntingdon Road
Cambridge CB3 0DL
☏ 0223 277314
*Collects and disseminates statistics
and information on the distribution
and numbers of animals and plants,
especially endangered species.*

World Conservation Union
(formerly IUCN — International Union
for the Conservation of Nature and
Natural Resources)
1196 Gland
Switzerland
☏ 010 41 22 64 9114
*An independent alliance of over 120
countries uniting on equal terms to
tackle conservation and the use of
natural resources, according to the
World Conservation Strategy (1980)
as a basis for priorities for action.*

**World Wide Fund for Nature International
(WWF)**
1196 Gland
Switzerland
☏ 010 41 22 64 71 81
*Campaigns and raises money for
conservation of wildlife and wild
places and promotes the wise use of
the earth's resources.*

Worldwatch Institute
1776 Massachusetts Avenue NW
Washington DC20036
USA
☏ 010 1 212 452 1999
*Informs governments and the public
of environmental issues, seen from a
global perspective with an
interdisciplinary approach.*

UK ORGANIZATIONS
General

Acid Rain Information Centre
Department of Environment and
Geographical Studies
Room 310, J. Dalton Extension
Chester Street
Manchester M1 5GD
☏ 061 228 6171
*Aims to promote the understanding
of causes and effects of acid rain
problems.*

Alternative Technology Association
Centre for Alternative Technology
Machynlleth
Powys SY20 9AZ
☏ 0654 2400
*Promotes the use and new ideas of
alternative technology in UK.*

Amateur Entomologists Society
22 Salisbury Road
Feltham
Surrey
TW13 5DP
☏ 081 890 3584
*Promotes the study of entomology
(insects), particularly for young
amateurs.*

Army Ornithological Society
Candlewick Cottage
Avenue Road
Fleet
Hampshire GU13 8NG
☏ 0252 617553
*Aims to encourage birdwatching in
the Army, promote discussions and
knowledge of ornithology in all its
aspects.*

**Association for the Protection of Rural
Scotland**
14a Napier Road
Edinburgh EH10 5AY
☏ 031 229 1081
*Exists to inform and influence public
opinion on the importance of
protecting Scotland's countryside.*

Association of British Wild Animal Keepers
12 Tackley Road
Eastville
Bristol BS5 6UQ
*Advises keepers of wild animals and
provides forum for discussion.*

**Association of National Parks and
Countryside Voluntary Wardens**
25 The High Gate
Newcastle upon Tyne NE3 4LS
☏ 091 285 8570
*A forum for wardens, to provide
information and to improve the
management of national parks.*

Barn Owl Trust
Waterleat
Ashburton
Devon TQ13 7HU
☏ 0364 53026
*Protects the barn owl and its habitat
in the UK.*

Bat Conservation Trust
c/o Conservation Foundation
1 Kensington Gore
London SW7 2AR
☏ 071 240 0933
*Aims to increase public awareness
and appreciation of bats.*

Bird Information Service
Tickers, High Street,
Cley-next-the-Sea,
Holt
Norfolk NR25 7RR
☏ 0263 741139
*Information on birds, particularly of
sightings of rare species.*

Black Environment Network
National Council for Voluntary
Organizations
26 Bedford Square
London WC1
☏ 071 636 4066
*Promotes environmental awareness
in the black community and supports
initiatives for active conservation
projects.*

Botanical Society of the British Isles (BSBI)
c/o Department of Botany
Natural History Museum
Cromwell Road
London SW7 5BD
☏ 071 589 6323
*An association for both amateurs and
professionals to study and conserve
British and Irish flowering plants and
ferns.*

British Antarctic Survey
High Cross
Madingley Road
Cambridge CB3 0ET
☏ 0223 61188
*Scientific research into Antarctica
and the Southern Ocean and also
research into the upper atmosphere
and ozone layer.*

British Arachnological Society
200 Abbey Lane
Sheffield S8 0BU
☏ 0742 351578
*Society for the study of spiders,
harvestmen and pseudoscorpions.*

**British Association for Shooting and
Conservation**
Marford Mill
Rossett
Clwyd LL12 0HL
☏ 0244 570881
*Promotes safety in the sport and
encourages the well-organized
management of habitats for the
benefit of all wildlife.*

**British Association of Nature
Conservationists**
85 Smirrels Road
Hall Green
Birmingham B28 0LA
☏ 021 778 5985
*A forum for discussion for all groups
and individuals concerned with
conservation.*

British Ecological Society
Burlington House
Piccadilly
London W1V 0LQ
☏ 071 434 2641
*Promotes research in ecology and
disseminates results.*

British Herpetological Society
c/o London Zoo
Regents Park
London NW1 4RY
☏ 071 722 3333
*Promotes the scientific study of
reptiles and amphibians.*

British Naturalists Association
48 Russell Way
Highham Ferrers
Northamptonshire NN9 8EJ
☏ 0933 314672
*Lobbies for the protection of wildlife
and of beautiful landscapes and
encourages the study of natural
history.*

British Ornithologists Union
c/o British Museum (Natural History)
Sub-department of Ornithology
Tring
Hertfordshire HP23 6AP
☏ 0442 890080
*Promotes the study of birds
worldwide and its main object since
its foundation is 'to further the
science of ornithology'.*

**British Trust for Conservation Volunteers
(BTCV)**
36 St Mary's Street
Wallingford
Oxon OX10 0EU
☏ 0491 39766
*Organizes practical conservation
work for volunteers of all ages, on a
local level for both rural and urban
areas.*

British Trust for Ornithology (BTO)
The Nunnery
Nunnery Place
Thetford
Norfolk IP24 2PU
☏ 0842 750050
*Encourages the serious study of
British wild birds and advises on their
conservation.*

British Waterfowl Association
Gill Cottage
New Gill,
Bishopdale
Leyburn
North Yorkshire DL8 3TQ
☏ 0969 663693
*Provides advice on keeping, breeding
and conserving all types of waterfowl.*

Butterfly Conservation Society
Tudor House
102 Chaveney Road
Quorn
Leicestershire LE12 8AD
☏ 0509 412870
*Encourages the protection of all
species of butterfly and sponsorship
of study and research.*

Care for the Wild
1 Ashfolds
Horsham
Rusper
West Sussex RH12 4QX
☏ 0293 871596
*Works to prevent cruelty and
suffering to wildlife.*

Centre for Urban Ecology
Birmingham Settlement
318 Summer Lane
Birmingham B19 3RL
☏ 021 359 7462
*An independent source of information
on the urban environment and its
improvement through correct policy.*

Common Ground
45 Shelton Street
London WC2H 9HJ
☏ 071 379 3109
*Promotes the importance of common
animals, plants and local landscapes.*

Conchological Society of Great Britain and Ireland
c/o Hon. Secretary
51 Wynchwood Avenue
Luton
Bedfordshire LU2 7HT
Devoted to the serious study of molluscs, from slugs to mussels.

Conservation Foundation
11A West Halkin Street
London SW1X 8JL
℡ 071 278 4736
Encourages industry and businesses to support and sponsor conservation by publicizing practical conservation projects.

The Conservation Trust
George Palmer Site
Northumberland Avenue
Reading RG2 7PW
℡ 0734 868442
Information and education service for the public of all ages. A focus for collection and dissemination of information relating to the global environment.

Council for Environmental Education (CEE)
School of Education
University of Reading
London Road
Reading
Berkshire RG1 5AQ
℡ 0734 875234 ext.218
Promotes and encourages environmental education, coordinating activities for over 60 national organizations, especially in the youth and school sectors.

Council for National Parks
45 Shelton Street
London WC2H 9HJ
℡ 071 240 3603
Formed by over 40 member organizations, the council undertakes research and publishes results, lobbies government and appears at public inquiries. Offers information and answers enquiries about National Parks.

Council for the Protection of Rural England (CPRE)
4 Hobart Place
London SW1W 0HY
℡ 071 235 9481
Promotes and encourages the improvement and protection of the countryside.

Council for the Protection of Rural Wales
Ty Gwyn
31 High Street
Welshpool
Powys SY21 7JP
℡ 0938 2525
(See CPRE — above)

The Country Trust
Denham Hill Farmhouse
Quainton
Aylesbury
Buckinghamshire HP22 4AN
℡ 0296 75454
A national educational charity which organizes and conducts visits to the British countryside for deprived inner city children.

Countryside Commission
John Dower House
Crescent Place
Cheltenham
Gloucestershire GL50 3RA
℡ 0242 521381
Advises central and local government on rural conservation & recreation. Has eight regional offices in England and Wales.

Countryside Commission for Scotland
Battleby
Redgorton
Perth PH1 3EW
℡ 0738 27821
(To be fused with the Nature Conservancy Council for Scotland to become Scottish Nature — see below).

Countryside Council for Wales
Plas Penrhos
Penrhos Road
Bangor
Gwynedd LL57 2LQ
℡ 0248 370444
Government organization for conservation in Wales.

Countryside Education Trust
John Montagu Building
Beaulieu
Hampshire SO42 7ZN
℡ 0590 612340
Works to make the country accessible to all and pomotes a caring and informed attitude to the countryside.

Countryside Venture
c/o Rural Enterprise Unit
Royal Agricultural Society
Stoneleigh
Warwickshire CV8 2LZ
℡ 0203 696969
Country training centres advise and train people in practical management and rural skills, and provide a focus for development and alternative land use possibilities.

Department of the Environment (Wildlife Division)
Tollgate House
Houlton Street
Bristol BS2 9DJ
℡ 0272 218233
Government body responsible for the administration of zoos, for environmental education, for conservation of species and their habitat, and for trade in endangered species.

Department of the Environment for Northern Ireland
Calvert House
23 Castle Place
Belfast BT1 1FY
℡ 0232 230560
The Countryside and Wildlife Branch is responsible for the acquisition and management of reserves and conservation in general.

Durrell Institute of Conservation and Ecology
University of Kent
Canterbury CT2 7NX
℡ 0227 475480
An academic institution associated with the University of Kent, undertaking research and post graduate teaching in conservation biology.

Edward Grey Institute of Field Ornithology
Department of Zoology
South Parks Road
Oxford OX1 3PS
℡ 0865 271275
An academic institution associated with the University of Oxford Department of Zoology.

Elefriends
Cherry Tree Cottage
Coldharbour
Dorking
Surrey RH5 6HA
℡ 081 682 1818
Elephant conservation society.

English Nature
Northminster House
Peterborough PE1 1UA
℡ 0733 413345
Government organization replacing the former NCC for England in April 1992.

Environment Council (formerly CoEnCo)
80 York Way
London N1 9AG
℡ 071 278 4736
Coordinates the activities of the voluntary conservation movement at a national level in Britain and provides a forum for discussion on major environmental issues.

Environmental Data Services
Finsbury Business Centre
40 Bowling Green Lane
London EC1R 0NE
℡ 071 278 7624
Information service for businesses.

Farming and Wildlife Trust
Stoneleigh
Kenilworth
Warwickshire CV8 2RX
℡ 0203 696699
Promotes the conservation of wildlife within the farmed countryside and advises farmers on how to incorporate conservation into modern agricultural techniques (through the Farming and Wildlife Advisory Groups — FWAGs).

Field Studies Council
Preston Montford
Montford Bridge
Shrewsbury SY4 1HW
Shropshire
℡ 0743 850674
Aims to promote understanding and appreciation of the natural environment and its wildlife through education, often in residential field courses.

Fish Conservation Centre
Easter Cringate
Stirling FK7 0QX
℡ 0786 51312
Promotes research and practical management projects for the conservation of fish.

Foreign Birdwatching Reports and Information Service
c/o Steve Whitehouse
5 Stanway Close
Blackpole
Worcester WR4 9XL
℡ 0905 54541
A reports and information service.

Forestry Commission
231 Corstophine Road
Edinburgh EH12 7AT
℡ 031 334 0303
The national forestry authority in the UK, administers legislation concerning forestry, and offers advice to private foresters.

Friends of the Earth (England, Wales and Northern Ireland) (FOE)
26–28 Underwood Street
London N1 7JQ
℡ 071 490 1555
Works to promote politics that will protect and improve the natural environment and to affect government policies on the environment by direct lobbying and public education.

Friends of the Earth (Scotland)
Bonnington Mill
72 Newhaven Road
Edinburgh
EH6 5QG
℡ 031 554 997
(See FOE — above)

Game Conservancy
Fordingbridge
Hampshire SP6 1EF
℡ 0425 652381
A research institute which also advises landowners and conservationists.

Greenpeace (UK)
Canonbury Villas
London N1 2PN
℡ 071 354 5100
Campaigns against abuse of the environment through direct non-violent action and lobbying.

The Hawk and Owl Trust
c/o Birds of Prey Section
Zoological Society of London
Regent's Park
London NW1 4RY
℡ 05283 2182
Conserves and encourages the study of birds of prey, especially those native to the UK.

Irish Wildbird Conservancy
Ruttledge House
8 Longford Place
Monkstown
Co. Dublin
℡ 0001 804 322
Promotes study and conservation of wild birds in Ireland.

League Against Cruel Sports
83–87 Union Street
London SE1 1SG
℡ 071 403 6155
Campaigns against sports which cause suffering to wildlife.

Living Earth Foundation
The Old Laundry
Ossington Buildings
Moxon Street
London W1M 3JD
℡ 071 487 3661
Concerned with conservation primarily through education. Also encourages projects in association with local business.

London Ecology Centre
45 Shelton Street
London WC2H 9HJ
℡ 071 379 4324
Advisory body for many ecological groups.

London Wildlife Trust
80 York Way
London N1 9AG
℡ 071 278 6612
Protects all areas of wildlife interest in Greater London and aims to promote awareness of the value of wildlife.

Lynx
PO Box 509
Dunmow
Essex CM6 1UH
℡ 0371 872016
Campaigns against the killing of animals for their fur.

Mammal Society
c/o Dept. of Zoology
University of Bristol
Woodlands Road
Bristol BS8 1UG
℡ 0272 272300
Promotes the study and conservation of mammals.

Marine Biological Association of the United Kingdom (MBA)
The Laboratory
Citadel Hill
Plymouth
Devon PL1 2PB
℡ 0752 221761
Promotes research that contributes to marine biological science; runs the Marine Pollution Information Centre.

Marine Conservation Society (MCS)
9 Gloucester Road
Ross-on-Wye
Herefordshire HR9 5BU
℡ 0989 66017
Solely concerned with coasts and offshore waters.

Media Natura
21 Tower Street
London WC2H 9SN
℡ 071 240 4936
An initiative from the media industry to help stimulate interest in environmental issues and to publicize conservation problems.

Men of the Trees
Turners Hill Road
Crawley Down
Crawley
West Sussex RH10 4HL
℡ 0342 712536
Worldwide tree planting and protection society.

The Monkey Sanctuary
Nr. Looe
Cornwall PL13 1NZ
℡ 05036 2532
Provides a home for a colony of grey woolly monkeys, offers advice about keeping monkeys in captivity and has a rehabilitation project to reintroduce the species in Amazonia.

National Birds of Prey Conservation Centre
Newent
Gloucestershire GL18 1JJ
℡ 0531 820286
Has a successful captive breeding collection of raptors and advises other zoos in the breeding of endangered species. Also makes people more aware of the need to conserve species of birds of prey.

National Federation of Badger Groups
7 London Road
Tetbury
Gloucestershire GL8 8JQ
℡ 0666 503419
Works for the protection, welfare and conservation of badgers.

National Federation of City Farms
Avon Environment Centre
Junction Road
Brislington
Bristol BS4 3JP
℡ 0272 719109
Promotes inner city farms where organic and sustainable farming methods are used.

National Rivers Authority
30–34 Albert Embankment
London SW1 7LL
℡ 071 820 0101
Protection and improvement of water quality and water environment in the UK.

National Trust Volunteer Unit
PO Box 12
Westbury
Wiltshire BA13 4NA
℡ 0373 826826
Organizes volunteer work, including working holidays.

National Trust for Scotland
5 Charlotte Square
Edinburgh EH2 4DU
℡ 031 226 5922
Preservation of land and buildings of national interest or natural beauty in Scotland. Runs the Thistle Camps for conservation holidays.

Otter Trust
Earsham
Nr Bungay
Suffolk NR35 2AF
℡ 0986 3470
Protects and conserves otters worldwide, especially the European otter.

Owl Study Group
c/o British Trust for Ornithology
Beech Grove
Tring
Hertfordshire HP23 5NR
℡ 044282 3461
A forum for exchange of ideas and knowledge for people interested in owls.

PANOS
9 White Lion Street
London N1 9PD
℡ 071 278 1111
Provides information on environmental issues mainly as briefings to the press and non-governmental organizations worldwide.

Plantlife
Natural History Museum
Cromwell Road
London SW7
℡ 071 938 9111
Protection of plants faced with extinction worldwide and in the UK. Recreation of lost habitats.

Rare Breeds Survival Trust
National Agricultural Centre
Kenilworth
Warwickshire CV8 2LG
℡ 0203 696551
Aims to increase stocks of rare breeds, keeps breeding registers, provides funds and holds workshops.

Reptile Protection Trust
College Gates
2 Deansway
Worcester WR1 2JD
℡ 0483 417550
Protection and conservation of all reptiles.

Royal Air Force Ornithological Society
General Secretary, Flt. Sgt. C J Sparks
RAF Signals Engineering Establishment, RAF Henlow
Bedfordshire SG16 6DN
Aims to encourage birdwatching in the RAF, especially on MOD properties.

Royal Naval Birdwatching Society
Hon. Secretary and Treasurer, Col. PJS Smith RM (Ret'd)
19 Downlands Way
South Wonston
Winchester
Hampshire SO21 3HS
℡ 0962 885 258
Promotes birdwatching in the Royal Navy; has developed a system of reporting the position and identity of birds at sea with standard sea report forms.

Royal Society for Nature Conservation (RSNC)
(The Wildlife Trusts Partnership)
The Green
Witham Park
Waterside South
Lincoln LN5 7JR
℡ 0522 544400
The umbrella group for the many local nature conservation trusts.

Royal Society for the Prevention of Cruelty to Animals (RSPCA)
The Causeway
Horsham
West Sussex RH12 1HG
℡ 0403 64181
Promotes kindness to animals and aims to prevent cruelty and suffering.

Royal Society for the Protection of Birds (RSBP)
The Lodge
Sandy
Bedfordshire SG19 2DL
℡ 0767 80551
Conserves and protects wild birds, promotes the appreciation of birds, manages nature reserves, conducts research, surveys and campaigns.

RSPB (Scotland)
17 Regent Terrace
Edinburgh EH7 5BN
℡ 031 557 3136
(See RSPB — above)

Scott Polar Research Institute (SPRI)
Lenfield Road
Cambridge CB2 1ER
℡ 0223 336540
A large and very specialist research unit and information service covering all aspects of the polar regions and adjacent areas.

Scottish Conservation Projects
(Dept BBC W)
Freepost
Stirling SK8 2BR
℡ 0786 79697
Aims to conserve and enhance the Scottish natural environment.

Scottish Natural Heritage
Battleby
Redgorton
Perth RH1 3EW
℡ 0738 27921
New organization replacing the Countryside Commission and Nature Conservancy Council in Scotland as from April 1992.

Scottish Society for the Prevention of Cruelty to Animals
19 Melville Street
Edinburgh EH3 7PL
℡ 031 225 6418/9
Represents animal welfare interests to government, local authorities and others.

Scottish Tree Trust
30 Edgemont Street
Glasgow G41 3EL
℡ 041 649 2462
Its aim is to plant and maintain native woodlands, involving young volunteers.

Scottish Wildlife Trust
25 Johnstone Terrace
Edinburgh EH1 2NH
tel 031 226 4602
Concerned with the conservation of Scotland's natural flora and fauna.

The Seabird Group
c/o RSPB
The Lodge
Sandy
Bedfordshire SG19 2DL
℡ 0767 680551
Concerned with the conservation of seabirds, coordinates census and monitoring work on breeding seabirds.

Sea Shepherd
PO Box 5
Ashford
Middlesex
℡ 0784 254846
Conservation of all marine wildlife.

Society of Wildlife Artists
Federation of British Artists
17 Carlton House Terrace
London SW1Y 5BD
℡ 071 930 6844
Annual exhibition of paintings in summer selected from an open submissions process. Membership by invitation only.

Tree Council
35 Belgrave Square
London SW1X 8QN
℡ 071 235 8854
Aims to improve the environment through the planting and care of trees.

Trust for Urban Ecology (TRUE)
PO Box 514
London SE16 1AS
℡ 071 237 9165
Aims to promote awareness and expertise in urban ecology, habitat creation and urban wildlife management.

Voluntary Service Overseas (VSO)
317 Putney Bridge Road
London SW15 2PN
℡ 081 780 1331
Organizes voluntary work worldwide.

Wader Study Group
44 The Pastures
Edlesborough
Dunstable
Bedfordshire LU6 2HL
An association of amateurs and professionals interested in wading birds.

Whale and Dolphin Conservation Society
19a James Street West
Bath
Avon BA1 2BT
℡ 0225 334511
Conservation of whales and dolphins and to promote public awareness.

Wildfowl and Wetlands Trust
Slimbridge
Gloucestershire GL2 7BT
℡ 0453 890333
Study and conservation of wildfowl and their habitats.

Wildlife Hospitals Trust
1 Pemberton Close
Aylesbury
Bucks HP21 7NY
℡ 0296 437373
Takes in and treats all species of British wild animal and bird. Educates others in the care and treatment of wild animals.

Wildlife Society
Alderbrook
Craven Road
Inkpen
Newbury
Berkshire RG1 0DX
Encourages the use of film and video to record and better understand the natural environment.

Wildlife Sound Recording Society
National Sound Archive
29 Exhibition Road
London SW7 2AS
℡ 071 589 6603
Provides advice in the recording of wildlife sounds.

Women's Environmental Network
22 Highbury Grove
London N5 2EA
℡ 071 354 8823
Deals with environmental problems that specifically concern women.

Woodlands Trust
Autumn Park
Dysart Road
Grantham
Lincs. NG31 6LL
℡ 0476 74297
Conservation of broadleaved and native British trees and creation of new woodlands.

Working Weekends on Organic Farms (WWOOF)
19 Bradford Road
Lewes
East Sussex BN7 1RB
Provides volunteers with the opportunity to try organic farming at first hand.

World of Water (WoW)
6 Fourth Avenue
Birmingham B29 7EU
℡ 021 472 7372
Aims to raise public awareness of value of water and its ecological use.

World Wide Fund for Nature UK (WWF–UK)
Panda House
Weyside Park
Godalming
Surrey GU7 1XR
℡ 0483 426444
Aims to conserve natural resources and promote sustainable activity through education, public policy, site protection, training and conservation of species.

Zoo Check
Cherry Tree Cottage
Coldharbour
Dorking
Surrey RH5 6HA
℡ 0306 712091
Monitors zoo conditions throughout the UK.

Political groups

Conservative Ecology Group
51 Stakes Hill Road
Waterlooville
Hampshire PO7 7LD
℡ 0735 222394
Informs MPs and others of developments in the international ecology movement.

Green Alliance
60 Chandos Place
London WC2N 4HG
℡ 071 836 0341
Encourages ecological awareness through all political life in the UK.

Green Party
10 Station Parade
Balham High Road
London SW12 9AZ
℡ 081 673 0045
Campaigns to promote harmony with nature and practice of sustainable economic activity.

Green Democrats (formerly Liberal Ecology Group)
19a Earls Court Square
London SW5 9BY
℡ 071 373 4631
Works to raise environmental and ecological issues within the party.

For children

Go Wild Club
Panda House
Weyside Park
Godalming
Surrey GU7 1XR
℡ 0483 426409
Junior branch of the WWF for members aged 7–18.

Mammal Society Youth Group
Harvest House
London Road
Reading RG1 5AS
℡ 0272 272300
Seeks to promote an interest in mammals, mainly for the under 18s.

Operation Raleigh
The Power House
Alpha Place
Flood Street
London SW3 5SZ
℡ 071 351 7541
An international charity which aims to develop the potential of people aged 17–25. It organizes conservation and community projects at home and abroad.

Watch Trust for Environmental Education Ltd (WATCH)
22 The Green
Nettleham
Lincoln LN2 2NR
℡ 0552 752326
Run by the RSNC to enable young people (up to 18 yrs.) to increase their knowledge of wildlife and to take an active part in conservation.

Wildfowl and Wetlands Centre
Martin Mere
Burscough
Ormskirk
Lancashire L40 0TA
℡ 0704 895181
Cares for injured and orphaned birds.

Young People's Trust for the Environment & Nature Conservation
95 Woodbridge Road
Guildford
Surrey GU1 4PY
℡ 0483 39600
An education and information service, especially to schools, on nature conservation issues.

Young Ornithologists Club (YOC)
The Lodge
Sandy
Bedfordshire SG19 2DL
℡ 0767 680551
The junior branch of the RSPB for any birdwatcher up to the age of 18.

VOLUNTEER WORK OPPORTUNITIES WITH ORGANIZATIONS

	Overseas Volunteers	Design and/or Illustration	Committee Work	Education (with adults and children)	Computers	Fundraising	Leafletting	Recording and Surveying	Sales, Stalls and Fairs	Stewards and Wardens	Administration/Office Work	Communicating with the public	Campaigning	Practical Conservation Work	Education (preparation of materials)	Guided Walks	Professional Skills	Research	Speaking at Lectures
Amateur Entomologists Society											●				●				●
Ark Environmental Foundation			●	●	●	●						●	●	●		●		●	●
British Naturalists Association			●			●			●	●		●					●	●	●
British Trust for Conservation Volunteers												●		●	●				
British Trust for Ornithology		●				●	●	●		●	●				●		●	●	●
Butterfly Conservation Society					●	●		●	●			●			●			●	●
Care for the Wild											●							●	
Centre for Urban Ecology											●								
Common Ground											●							●	
Council for National Parks			●			●				●		●	●	●				●	●
Council for the Protection of Rural England						●	●		●		●	●	●						
Countryside Education Trust		●		●	●	●	●	●	●	●	●	●		●	●	●	●	●	●
Countryside Venture					●	●	●		●		●				●		●	●	
Earthwatch (Europe)	●																		
Friends of the Earth	●	●			●	●	●				●				●		●	●	
Gaia Foundation			●	●	●	●					●	●		●		●	●	●	●
Greenpeace						●			●		●								
Hawk and Owl Trust						●			●	●									
International Council for Bird Preservation	●	●		●							●						●	●	
International Primate Protection League	●					●	●				●	●	●						
Living Earth		●	●	●		●					●			●			●	●	
Marine Conservation Society			●			●		●	●		●						●		
Men of the Trees			●		●		●						●	●	●			●	
National Trust for Scotland			●			●		●					●	●					
National Trust Volunteer Unit				●				●		●	●		●		●	●			
Operation Raleigh	●	●	●	●	●	●	●	●	●	●	●	●	●	●	●	●	●	●	●
People's Trust for Endangered Species		●				●	●												
Plantlife								●	●			●							
Population Concern				●	●			●		●									●
Reptile Protection Trust				●	●	●	●		●										
Royal Society for Nature Conservation		●	●	●	●	●	●	●	●	●	●	●	●	●	●	●	●	●	●
Royal Society for the Prevention of Cruelty to Animals		●	●	●	●	●	●		●		●	●	●	●			●		●
Royal Society for the Protection of Birds										●			●	●					
Scottish Conservation Projects		●				●	●	●		●		●	●	●			●		
Sea Shepherd		●				●	●		●			●	●		●			●	
Trust for Urban Ecology		●		●	●				●	●	●			●	●		●	●	
Voluntary Service Overseas	●																		
Wildlife Hospitals Trust				●															
Women's Environmental Network		●		●	●	●	●		●		●	●	●		●		●	●	
Woodland Trust										●				●					●
Working Weekends on Organic Farms											●								●
World of Water	●	●	●	●	●	●					●	●	●	●	●		●	●	●
World Wide Fund for Nature			●				●	●		●									
Zoo Check				●	●	●		●			●								●

COMPETITION DETAILS

(Not all competitions are run every year)

The Ansorge Award
Organized by the Amateur Entomologists Society for the Best Junior Exhibit at the Society's Annual Exhibition. Entries in October.

Bird Yearlist
Sponsoring competition run by the British Trust for Ornithology which provides a booklet for competitors' bird count over a year.
Entries in January, results February.
First prize: Pair of Leica binoculars worth £650.

The Blake Shield
Run by The British Naturalists Association for groups of people 8-16 years with adult leaders in natural history projects. Entries in June.
First prize: Residential visit to a Field Centre.

BP Conservation Expedition Award
ICBP, the FFPS and The Conservation Expedition Competition offer a total of £20,000 in grant funding for expeditions involving people in the following categories: Tropical Forests, Wetland, Oceanic Islands & Marine and Globally Threatened Species.
First prize: £3000 (half of which should be intended for local people in the relevant countries who helped with the expedition).

The Hammond Award
Organized by the Amateur Entomologists Society for the most useful article published during the year in the Society's bulletin.

Natural Chords
Competition to find a song for nature run by the Worldwide Fund for Nature. Entries in March 1992, results in June

the same year.
First prize: £500.

Nature Writing
Essay competition run by BBC *Wildlife* Magazine in association with BBC Radio 4's Natural History Programme. Entries by May, results August.
First prize: £1000.

Wildlife Poet of the Year
Organized by BBC *Wildlife* Magazine, with BBC Radio 4's *Poetry Please* and Radio 5's *Talking Poetry*. Entries by January, results May.
First prize: £500.

Wildlife Photographer of the Year.
Organized by BBC Wildlife Magazine, The Natural History Museum and the Fauna & Flora Preservation Society. Entries by June, results August, exhibition December.
First prize: £400.

FURTHER READING

1990 IUCN Red List of Threatened Animals, IUCN, 1990.

The Environment Digest, Panther House, 38 Mount Pleasant WC1X 0AP

ITN Factbook, Michael O'Mara Books Ltd, 1990.

Attenborough, David, *The Living Planet*, Collins, 1984.

Attenborough, David, *Trials of Life*, Collins, 1990.

Bellamy, David, *How Green Are You?*, Frances Lincoln, 1991.

Burton, John A, *Rare Mammals of the World*, Collins, 1987.

Button, John (comp.), *Green Pages*, Macdonald Optima, 1988.

Cawardine, Mark, *WWF Environment Handbook*, Macdonald & Co, 1990.

Cowell, Sarah (ed.), *Who's Who in the Environment*, Environment Council, 1990.

Day, Alan J., *The Annual Register 1990*, Longman, 1990.

Durrell, Lee, *State of the Ark*, Gaia Books Ltd, 1986.

Elkington, John and Hailes, Julia, *The Green Consumer Guide*, Victor Gollancz Ltd, 1989.

Frisch, Monia, *Directory for the Environment*, 3rd edition, Green Print, 1990.

Gould, David and Heald, Henrietta, *Chronicle of the Year 1990*, Longman, 1990.

Hare, Tony, *Save Our Earth: Rainforest Destruction*, Gloucester Press, 1990.

Hare, Tony, *Save Our Earth: Habitat Destruction*, Gloucester Press, 1991.

Lean, Geoffrey, Hinrichsen, Don, and Markham, Adam, *WWF Atlas of the Environment*, Arrow Books, 1990.

Mountfort, Guy, *Rare Birds of the World*, Collins, 1988.

Porritt, Jonathon (ed.), *Friends of the Earth Handbook*, Macdonald Optima, 1987.

Tudge, Colin, *Global Ecology*, Natural History Museum, 1991.

Unwin Animal Library, (6 vols), George Allen and Unwin, 1984.

Magazines

BBC Wildlife Magazine

Birds (the magazine for the Royal Society for the Protection of Birds)

British Wildlife Magazine

Green Magazine

New Scientist

Oryx (the magazine for the Fauna and Flora Preservation Society)

Plantlife Newsletter

WWF News

INDEX

Numbers in *italics* refer to illustrations

PICTURE ACKNOWLEDGEMENTS

(t = top; b = bottom; l = left; r = right)

Alan Atkinson/BTCV 147

Jill Bailey/Ecofeatures 156 (both), 156–7.

Adrian Barnett 23.

BBC Natural History Unit 164b, 165t, 168,173t.

Rob Bowker/BTCV 149.

Chester Zoo 178, 179.

Bruce Coleman Ltd B & C Alexander 90–1; Jen & Des Bartlett 35t; E & P Bauer 29, 38–9, 63, 90; Mark N Boulton 127t; R I M Campbell 167; John Cancalosi 126, 133; Alain Compost 13bl, 67, 69t; Gerald Cubitt 108t, 109t, 182t; Peter Davey 160; Geoff Dore 95; Dr Inigo Everson 40t; Jeff Foott 28b, 40b, 93; B & D W Frith 69r; J L G Grande 78; Peka Helo 42t; David Hughes 31r, b; Gordon Langsbury 76; George McCarthy 71r; John Mackinnon 14, 19t, 170; Luiz Claudio Marigo 68b; M P Price 79; Hans Reinhard 30, 71l, 100, 158b; Peter Ward 52t; Rod Williams 68r; Joseph van Wormer 68l; WWF/Timm Rautert 16; WWF/Kojo Tanaka 18; Gunter Ziesler 6–7, 77.

Mark Edwards/Still Pictures 118–19.

The Environmental Picture Library Vanessa Miles 142t, 146.

John Frost 136b.

Gamma/Frank Spooner Pictures 120; Leroy 165b; Noel Quidu 112, 112–13, 116t; L van der Stockt 114, 115 (both).

Jane Goodall Institute 166bl.

Greenpeace/Morgan 137.

Charlie Hamilton-James 194, 195 (both), 196 (both), 197, 198 (both), 199 (both).

David Haring 25, 70.

Hulton Picture Company 166br.

ICBP 161t.

Jersey Wildlife Preservation Trust Phillip Coffey 166t, 182b, 183.

© Nancy Knight 1990 26, 27.

Terence Lambert 184, 185, 186 (all), 187.

Longleat 181.

Lynx 138 (both).

Russell A Mittermeier/Conservation International 20 (both).

Stephen D Nash/Conservation International 24.

The Natural History Museum 174, 175, 176 (both), 177.

NHPA © Jany Sauvanet/NHPA 22; © Stephen Dalton/NHPA 56bl, br; ©ANT (M F Soper)/NHPA 69b.

Oxford Scientific Films © David Curl 31t.

Panos Pictures Heidi Bradner 141; Roderick Johnson 118; Nick Robinson 36–7.

G Pinkhassov/Magnum 123t.

Planet Earth Pictures K Ammann 81, 129b, 135bl, 155, 172; D Barrett 127b; J R Bracegirdle 73tr, 106–7; Jim Brandenburg 125; Franz J. Camenzind 16–17, 66–7; Mary Clay 19b; Norman Cobley 43; Richard Coomber 74–5, 80, 96t, 102–3; Peter David 44–5, 46 (both), 47b, 49b 52b; G Deichmann/Transglobe 33; John Downer 168–9; Nigel Downer 159; Geoff du Feu 53t; Wayne Harris 58; Hans Christian Heap 35b; Robert Hessler 48; Bill Howes 153b; Antony Joyce 96b; Robert Jureit 64, 120–1; Jon Kenfield 61b; James King 49t; Ken King 59b; John Lythgoe 152; John & Gillian Lythgoe 116b; Gillian Lythgoe 94t; Michael McKinnon 110–11; Jeannie Mackinnon 53b; David P Maitland 56; Richard Matthews 1, 38, 61t, 98–9, 108b, 163b, 188; Jerry Mayes 132–3; Roger Mear 42b; Bora Merdsoy 88–9; Andrew Mounter 21; Duncan Murrell 41; Ernest Neal 97b; Jesus Perez 140; Doug Perrine 54, 143, 144–5; K Puttock 10, 73b; Andy Rouse 94b; David E Rowley 32, 55; Rod Salm 91, 135t, 153t; Philip Sayers 39; Peter Scoones 82–3; Jonathan Scott 57b, 60–1, 122t, 129t, 139b, 154; Anup Shah 66; Clare Shorter 34b; William M Smithey, Jr 150, 151; Peter Stephenson 122b; P V Tearle 50; Nigel Tucker 65; Herwarth Voigtmann 85t, 171; Jan Walencik 101; James D Watt 58–9; Bill Wood 62; Norbert Wu 47t; Munesuke Yamamoto 15.

Purdy & Matthews 2–3, 8–9, 48–9, 57t, 73tl, 135br, 163t, 189, 190–1, 192, 193 (both).

RSPB 142b, 148; C H Gomersall 158t.

Survival Anglia Terry Andrewartna 97t; Jan & Des Bartlett 34t, 104 (both); Joel Bennett 92t; Joe B Blossom 128; Caroline Brett 130; Bruce Davidson 13t, 173b; Jeff Foott 13 (br), 28t, 68t, 124; Mary Grant 109b; Malcolm Penny 92b; Michael Pitts 132; Dieter & Mary Plage 11, 131; Joan Root 139t; Arjan Singh 60b.

Whipsnade Wild Animal Park 180 (both).

Wildfowl & Wetlands Trust Jonathan Leach 164.

Elizabeth Wood 84 (both), 85b, 86, 87 (both).

WWF-UK 136t; Mauri Rautikari 161b.

NORTH
AMERICA

ATLANTIC
OCEAN

PACIFIC
OCEAN

SOUTH
AMERICA